THE SIESTA AND
THE MIDNIGHT SUN

Jessa Gamble

VIKING
CANADA

To my father, who taught me to find work that feels like play

VIKING CANADA

Published by the Penguin Group

Penguin Group (Canada), 90 Eglinton Avenue East, Suite 700, Toronto, Ontario,
Canada M4P 2Y3 (a division of Pearson Canada Inc.)

Penguin Group (USA) Inc., 375 Hudson Street, New York, New York 10014, U.S.A.
Penguin Books Ltd, 80 Strand, London WC2R 0RL, England
Penguin Ireland, 25 St Stephen's Green, Dublin 2, Ireland
(a division of Penguin Books Ltd)
Penguin Group (Australia), 250 Camberwell Road, Camberwell, Victoria 3124,
Australia (a division of Pearson Australia Group Pty Ltd)
Penguin Books India Pvt Ltd, 11 Community Centre, Panchsheel Park,
New Delhi–110 017, India
Penguin Group (NZ), 67 Apollo Drive, Rosedale, Auckland 0632,
New Zealand (a division of Pearson New Zealand Ltd)
Penguin Books (South Africa) (Pty) Ltd, 24 Sturdee Avenue, Rosebank,
Johannesburg 2196, South Africa

Penguin Books Ltd, Registered Offices: 80 Strand, London WC2R 0RL, England

1 2 3 4 5 6 7 8 9 10 (RRD)

Manufactured in the U.S.A.

Library and Archives Canada Cataloguing in Publication

Gamble, Jessa
The siesta and the midnight sun : how our bodies experience time / Jessa Gamble.

Includes index.
ISBN 978-0-670-06511-0

1. Biological rhythms. 2. Time—Social aspects.
3. Experience. I. Title.

QH527.G34 2011   571.7'7   C2011-903928-1

Visit the Penguin Group (Canada) website at **www.penguin.ca**

Special and corporate bulk purchase rates available;
please see **www.penguin.ca/corporatesales**
or call 1-800-810-3104, ext. 2477.

contents

foreword

BY JAY INGRAM

THE IDEA OF A BIOLOGICAL CLOCK has always seemed to me to be counter-intuitive. Clocks are nothing if not mechanical: In their initial incarnation they were elaborate arrays of gears, pendulums and chimes, and while much more subtle and digital today, they nonetheless remain instruments undeniably inanimate. To match that image with the idea of flesh and blood requires a giant leap of imagination. Yet, the evidence that we contain clocks that time our activities is undeniable.

I think that accounts for their fascination: How could the wet chemistry of the brain, where actions and thoughts seem so unrelated to timekeeping, nonetheless be ticking our lives away? How could an escapement be a protein, or a spring a biochemical cycle? And these are only the beginning questions: If indeed there is a biological clock (or two), how are they set? Or reset?

Trying to understand how such a living clock could possibly be made represents the bottom-up approach. Top-down is much more intuitive. Yes, there is plenty of evidence that we are guided by our clock(s). We get drowsy at night, and wake refreshed in the morning. We cross time zones and immediately realize that something has gone wrong, and only feel revived after hours or even days in the new location. There are more traffic accidents the day after Daylight Savings Time begins. The night shift is disruptive. Something is keeping time.

You'll notice that it is only when the daily routine is disrupted that we realize that there are timekeepers in our bodies—sticking to the daily routine does nothing to bring that to our attention. As Jessa makes clear in this book, becoming aware of such disturbances is only the first step: Reacting to them by creating time-defined cultural practices has differentiated peoples around the world for as far back as we can trace, and tinkering with those disturbances, turning them on or off, can lead to scientific understanding.

And who better to link these together than someone who has lived much of her life in Canada's far north, where the sun and the length of day change so dramatically from one season to another? (Although in apparent anticipation of this book, even when a Torontonian she managed to disrupt her own biological clock by working two jobs, one of which required starting work at 3 A.M. As she says, "The hardest part of the job was keeping my eyes open.") It is this combination of personal experience, science and cultural observation that makes this book much richer than any one-dimensional view of body time.

And of course its appeal is all the greater because we all have our own personal stories to tell. Mine is this: Whenever I have to wake up at an unusual time (especially one that is significantly earlier than I am used to) I seem to wake up about five minutes before the alarm. I say "seem" because it is all too tempting to ignore those times when I don't. But I know it happens frequently, and I'm not the first person to be curious about this. In the 1920s, a British physician, Winslow Hall, recorded one hundred attempts to wake up at a predetermined time, and was able to nail it exactly eighteen times. But Hall might have been a rare case, because he had a similarly acute sense of time when awake, being able to guess accurately within three minutes, forty percent of the time. (Sadly, he left no details of exactly how these self-experiments were done.)

But how can anyone wake up at a predetermined time? If indeed the hormones adrenocorticotropin and cortisol rise as waking nears, how can simply telling yourself to wake trigger those hormones?

For me it is these delicious personal puzzles that make the biological clock so fascinating, but until I read this book I was ignorant of how far-reaching its effects are, and have been. We humans have evolved at the behest of our clocks, but we, just one species, are a relatively insignificant example. The entire tree of life runs on time. And that is something worth knowing, so read on.

clock-punching lab rats

In the late 1990s, when Rob McDonald arrived at the University of Toronto to take up his tenure-track position in psychology, he opened the door to the neurology laboratory he had been promised and found a grotty carpeted room with a sink. The university had hired a cohort of psychology professors in the 1960s, when a cognitive model—the human mind as a computer—had been all the rage. There were no real laboratories assigned to the psychology department, as it had never moved on from the computer model to the squishy, rat-infested world of brain science. McDonald shook his head in disbelief, tacked up a band poster of The Who and got to work on his research.

He soon gained a reputation for nonconformity, which he blames on the institution's discomfort with youth; still in his thirties, McDonald was one of the university's youngest professors. I suspect his notoriety had more to do with rumours that he told his classes all drugs should be legal and with the fact that he used his undergraduate biological psychology courses to show seemingly irrelevant movies (Noam Chomsky's *Manufacturing Consent* or *Harold and Maude*) that he felt all students should see in their formative years. Nevertheless, the strength of his research brought international recognition to the department.

It was in his Neurochemical Bases of Behaviour class that I first heard the words *circadian rhythms*. In the lab below our feet, rodents were held in constantly dim light with nothing but a running wheel to entertain them. Dr. McDonald clicked to a new slide, and I saw a histogram—a graph used to plot frequency data—that would change the course of my life: time of day on one axis, days of the experiment on the other and running wheel activity plotted in the middle. These rats got up at three in the afternoon and packed it in at one in the morning every day, as if they were government clock-punchers. As proof that they weren't being tipped off to the time, the graph showed them drifting to an ever-so-slightly later schedule every day, like teenagers on vacation. These animals were running on their own amazingly precise clocks, only parting with the standard time by a difference of minutes per day.

Immediately, I signed up for the next year's circadian rhythms course and went to work at Dr. McDonald's lab, performing surgeries for which I was hideously underqualified and testing brain-damaged rats to see whether their injuries interfered with their internal clocks. Later, we performed perfusions, a special procedure for killing a rat without changing its brain, done by pumping formaldehyde into the still-beating heart of an unconscious animal.

Buried in a dank sub-basement full of cockroaches, I studied these timekeeping systems in rats as a research assistant during my student years. Next to a concrete room full of pecking Burmese Red junglefowl—someone else's experiment—was a row of cages kept in constantly dim light. The wire cages were lined with newspaper and wood chips, each with a water bottle and food dispenser attached to the bars. Each cage contained one rat and one exercise wheel, with a little tunnel for the rat to sleep in and hide out in. McDonald was allergic to rats, so he rarely set foot in the lab. This left us, the students, to perform the experiments ourselves, learning on the job.

I became quite familiar with rat behaviour during my time in that lab. The poor things were housed individually—a no-no even then, according to the generally accepted standards of humane care, particularly as it affected a profoundly social animal—and they seemed to go about their day pretty randomly. Watching the rats, I could never predict what one of them would do next. It might gnaw neurotically at the bars for a few seconds and then scamper over to the other side of the cage and rise on its back paws, sniffing the air. It might take a quick nip of water and then climb onto the running wheel for a trot, stopping and starting at invisible cues.

The running wheels were hooked up to a machine that recorded activity, and the printouts from these readings told a completely different story: The rats' actions were *not* random. On each graph, the data was spookily identical. At three in the afternoon on the first day, the running wheel started spinning. With little breaks in the reading, where the rat had hopped off, the data continued to show activity until one in the morning, when there was a long break punctuated by short blips of wheel-running through the morning. It was the same each day, this exact pattern.

Except that every day they started just a few minutes later. As if their watches were ever so slightly slow, the rats followed a twenty-four-and-a-bit-hour cycle, with some rats following a fractionally slower internal clock than others. This slippage was the proof I needed that my rats were running on circadian time. From the Latin *circa*, or "around," and *diem*, or "day," *circadian time* is the body's internal time zone, which gradually loses reference to the standard time-zone clock time if given no dawn to reset it.

Rather than starting their day's activities according to some external cue—a de facto alarm clock—the rats must have been following an inner schedule: The constant light gave them no externally defined day or night to live by.

Of course, in the wild, the rats would have changing levels of sunlight to reset their clocks every day while they were out foraging, keeping them from drifting away from Earth time. The biological timekeeping is only an estimation, after all, and not as accurate as the planet's constant rotation rate. The key function of this internal timekeeping device is to allow the animal to anticipate environmental events—like the arrival of food—rather than becoming aware of them only after they've occurred, potentially missing out on the action. The idea is that the predator is in sync with its prey. The plants are in sync with the sunlight. Sometimes the outside world is hard to interpret, though. Phytoplankton that spend their days deep in the ocean need to rise for the night, but they are beyond the sunlight's reach: They need an internal cue to clue them in to nightfall.

Known variously as *biological rhythms*, *chronobiology*, *biological timekeeping* and *chronomics*, the science of circadian rhythms is so embryonic it doesn't yet have an agreed-upon name. Knowledge from all of the hard sciences—and recently some of the soft ones—is only now coming together to answer questions about the temporal dimension of life. But I'm left gobsmacked by some of the studies that make up our early knowledge about circadian rhythms; I'm continually amazed at how universal these natural clocks are and, even more so, at how precise they can be.

From the single-celled bacterium to the blue whale, all life on Earth evolved under a common condition: the rotation of the planet. We have no immediate perception of the Earth's rotation, of course, but the sun's passage across the sky is testament to the whirling environment that gave rise to life. Through all the climatic shifts over the millennia—beginning with the warm, soupy seas and atmospheres devoid of oxygen—day and night have been the steadiest constants in the evolution of plants and animals. Rather than simply reacting to each sunrise and sunset as if it were a surprise, living beings are hard-wired to cycle with the planet using an internal clock. All multicellular and some unicellular life shows circadian rhythmicity. This phenomenon could very well be the most ubiquitous and overlooked in the natural world.

This branch of science as we know it was launched in 1960 at the Cold Spring Harbor Symposia on Quantitative Biology, in Long Island, New York. It was the twenty-fifth symposium and the theme was "Biological Clocks." It was the largest Cold Spring Harbor symposium up to that time, with over three hundred scientists in attendance. Researchers who had been working in parallel for years, grinding away in animal labs and field stations around the world, discovered that they had intellectual company they knew nothing about. Finally, they could compare notes with others who shared their passions. Ideas clashed and combined, converging from dozens of disciplines.

The organizing-committee list reads like a who's who of the field. Erwin Bünning gave an opening address, summarizing developments since his breakthrough demonstrations of the existence of internal biological rhythms and drawing on his recently published, seminal book *The Physiological Clock*. Jürgen Aschoff proposed a list of components in a circadian system, and Patricia DeCoursey laid out the biological rhythms of rodents. Colin Pittendrigh presented a theoretical model of circadian rhythms that would come to lead thinking in this area for decades. What I would give to have been there! This work on the existence of internal timekeeping revealed a uniting force within all life, promising to give us insight into our own days and nights, the rhythms that rule our activities, our health and even, to some extent, our thoughts. My research into the body clock has led me to real-ize the universality of its influence, which has implications for all human beings both as individuals and as a group—for how we live our lives and how we will live in the future.

After graduating, I found myself more drawn to writing about science than to conducting research, but even as my work took me in a different direction, those rats were never far from my mind. It seemed to me there was a hidden order in nature that was linked directly to the solar system's workings. All living things contained clocks, and humans were no exception. Given that we were ruled by these forces too, I wondered why there was so little talk about the biology that scheduled our days and nights before we ever opened our Daytimers. If there were any demonstration of Darwin's great revelation of our oneness with nature, it was here in everyday life, in the daily rhythms of our families, our pets, our plants. Circadian rhythms became a kind of specialty of mine within my science-writing career, and I started to build a sub-niche for myself as a journalist in the field.

The same running-wheel graph I had marvelled over in McDonald's rat lab could have been made from the activity of the cockroaches that infested the basement. After all my talk of circadian rhythms' universality, the idea that insects also adhere to a biologically deter-mined schedule should come as no surprise. And it turns out that people have actually done the experiments to prove it, with tiny running wheels. What the experiment found is that cockroaches go for a two- or three-hour run just after dark; they're what we call a crepuscular animal, one whose prime activity occurs around dusk and dawn. They live in the twilight zone. Many of the animals we think of as nocturnal are actually crepuscular; it's just that we don't notice their inactivity in the dead of night because we ourselves are mostly diurnal—we live for the dawn of another day. If the cockroaches are kept in constant light, their activity graph—starting with their active period in the evening—shifts a few minutes later every day, just like the rats. This shows that the insects have their own internal clocks and are not just reacting to light changes. Cockroaches do react, dramatically, to light in the sense that they're photophobic—they scurry for cover when the lights are turned on. But their cyclical behaviour is triggered by something else.

In biology, a clock is a circular chain of chemical reactions that takes about twenty-four hours to come back to its starting point and begin again. The biologically inclined among you might find this notion a little specious when it's extended to include animals that are not warm-blooded. It's all well and good to have a chemical clock in rats and other mammals whose body temperature is relatively constant—metabolism keeps the internal temperature steady regardless of the weather outside, and chemical reactions like those in the chemical clock can tick along at a steady pace. It's another thing altogether to measure time using the speed of chemical reactions in a creature that does not use metabolism to maintain body temperature, swinging wildly from nighttime cold to daytime baking heat, with vacillations depending on shade and weather. The usual rule is that in cold-blooded creatures the rate of metabolism doubles with every 10-degree Celsius rise in internal temperature. The warmer it gets, the faster chemical reactions occur and the faster bodily functions happen. That's why, other than having a period of roughly twenty-four hours and being able to cycle continuously with no reference to outside time, circadian clocks also must be temperature-compensated.

When an animal's body gets colder, circadian systems make up for the general slowdown.

The circadian system is the structure a plant or animal can use to plot out its priorities—be they eating, resting, growing or hiding—during the day and night. There is a day and night happening out there in the world, a planet rotating while in orbit around the sun, but there is also a day within. The internal day usually passes in tandem with the external day, but must not be mistaken for a facet of it. They're not the same thing.

Circadian rhythms are shared by every animal and plant on the planet—indeed, by every known organism that has two or more cells, and even by some that have only one cell. Without this innate ability to gauge time, animals lose the coordinated functioning of their bodily systems. Like an orchestra with one conductor for the string section, another for the winds and a third for percussion, a body without a central clock works against itself. This has been borne out in research on fruit flies, which, when deprived of circadian function—by destroying their circadian system or severing the system's ties with the rest of the body—suffer a drastically shorter lifespan.

Circadian rhythms are so advantageous they've actually evolved at least four times over the course of life's evolution. Though mouse and fly genes show that a common ancestor contained a circadian clock 700 million years ago—before animals split into vertebrates and invertebrates—the molecular processes in plants, fungi and bacteria are all different, suggesting they evolved separately. Still, they all share a similar mechanism; namely, a negative feedback loop—a chain of cause and effect that circles around to exactly where it started. Here's how this works: Genes in a cell instruct it to produce certain proteins, but when enough of those proteins have been made that there's a critical concentration of them in the cell, the genes are switched off until the proteins have been broken down. Then they start all over again, instructing the cells to make new proteins. High protein levels in turn trigger chemical signals that rouse the body for daytime activities.

If a clock is anything with a regular oscillation, then plants and animals that regularly follow their internal clocks through daily routines can themselves become clocks. A beautiful example is the flower clock: Different types of flower open at various times of day to catch the activities of their specific *vector species*, the birds and flying insects that distribute pollen from flower to flower. The more precisely aligned the flowers are with their pollen-carriers and the more separated they are in time from other species, the more efficiently they can reproduce. So in any given place, there are likely to be flowers that open, serially, at most hours of the day.

The famous eighteenth-century biologist Carolus Linnaeus proposed the concept of a flower clock in which plants could be placed in a circle, like a clock face, according to the time of day they flowered. Then when people took walks in the garden they could tell the hour of the day by glancing at which of the flowers was open. He suggested dandelions for 5 A.M., garden lettuce for 7 A.M., scarlet pimpernel for 8 A.M. and sand spurrey for 9 A.M. However good the concept, its application was tricky to apply, what with the complexity of factors leading to a flower's opening during different parts of the season. Lately, though, professional gardeners have set up ingenious examples in Switzerland, Iran, Scotland and Mexico—even in Michael Jackson's Neverland Ranch. They tend to have actual moving hands, though, to make the reading easier.

How well the skillful gard'ner drew
Of flow'rs and herbs this dial new,
Where from above the milder sun
Does through a fragrant zodiac run;
And as it works, th' industrious bee
Computes its time as well as we.
How could such sweet and wholesome hours
Be reckon'd but with herbs and flow'rs!

The poet Andrew Marvell could not have known from his vantage point in the seventeenth century how right he was about those bees. The more we learn about bees, the more flabbergasting their abilities appear to be, and many of these abilities relate to their daily task of visiting several types of flower in different places, each at a specific time of day. They can be trained to visit feeding stations in strategically placed locations, each station at a certain hour.

We know they can do this not only because they demonstrate it in their flight, but also because they come back and dance about it. If it sounds funny to think that an insect can dance about something, just watch a bee come into a hive and jig around. Every waggle and buzz communicates specific knowledge about the location of a food source, and the observing bees act on that information as if they've just read a detailed manual. The reporting bee tells the others about the angle of the sun relative to the direction in which they have to travel to reach the food. Because the Earth moves in relation to the sun, the bee corrects 15 degrees for each hour that's passed since it flew the course itself. When recounting the distance from the hive to the food, the bee actually communicates the time it took to get to the food—it even notes more time for the same distance if there was a headwind.

Though bees can be trained to fly to a certain place every twenty-four hours, they cannot be taught to go there every, say, nineteen hours. The extent to which they can be trained ends where the biological system's assumptions begin, and a twenty-four-hour day is rigged right into the cells. If you try to train them by putting food out every forty-eight hours—still at the same time, just every two days—they will check the station every twenty-four hours.

The ways life applies its timekeeping abilities are as numerous as its species. As life first arose and the atmosphere was not yet the shield it is now against damaging UV rays, the sun was a major hazard for bacteria. Even now, a few hours of exposure around noon is almost guaranteed to produce a handful of genetic errors in dividing cells. Many bacteria, therefore, use their circadian systems to shut off their cell division for the hours of strongest ultraviolet exposure.

The humblest of beings, the single-celled euglena, is ruled by the tides, which, on average, repeat every twelve hours and twenty-five minutes. When the tide is in, the euglena burrows into the mud to protect itself from the powerful water surge. An internal clock in its protoplasm, independent of light and temperature, dictates when it will start working to free itself from its self-made cave and emerge into the air—just as the tide has gone out. There in the sunshine it can take the opportunity of a calm environment to photosynthesize.

Daily *vertical migration*—movement from the surface to the depths and back—is standard practice among tidal creatures. A flatworm rises to the surface during daytime low tide to expose the green algae that lives within it to sunlight. The worm digests some of the algae even as the rest continues to thrive inside it. The algae need the sun and the worm needs the algae. The worm itself .

would starve if it were too long in darkness because the algae would die first.

With circadian rhythms, vertical migrators can anticipate when they need to be at the surface. If their timing is off and they're late—because, for example, they wait for the sun to rise in the sky (if, indeed, they can detect sunlight from the depths)—they would be unable to extract the full benefit from its rays. Preparation is everything when there's strong competition for maximum energy and efficiency—a constant in the cutthroat world of evolution. The environment has predictable properties that are coordinated with the time of day, and so the organisms living in this environment should have predictable priorities linked to the hour. Nitrogen-fixing bacteria, for example, perform two key functions: They take nitrogen from the atmosphere and convert it into a form usable by plants, and they photosynthesize to glean energy from sunlight. The problem is that they cannot do these two things at the same time. An enzyme used in nitrogen-fixation is too sensitive to the oxygen produced in photosynthesis, so the bacteria use their circadian systems to help them alternate between photosynthesis—in the daytime, of course—and nitrogen-fixing at night. If they are taken out of the day–night light cycle, they continue obliviously to switch back and forth between the two tasks.

Evening primroses, which exude an alluring scent to their evening pollinators, need time to produce their seductive oils. It is their circadian rhythms that ensure the process begins long before the insects alight for night. Daily rhythms are as fundamental to survival as is reproduction. Fish whose eyes shift into daytime vision need almost half an hour to make the transition. When they hear the biological alarm sound from their internal clocks, their eyes start readying for light they can't yet see. In this way, they get an extra half-hour of visual acuity every day—a make-or-break feature over the course of a fish lifetime, let alone over the millennia of evolutionary time.

Independent of the outside world, a circadian rhythm has a regular tempo, fluctuating in a constant period of roughly twenty-four hours. The flower that folds its petals every night keeps track of the time using a chemical oscillation. The chemical process in each of its cells takes a day to circle around to the start again, triggering the flower's closing even without temperature changes or darkness.

To a large extent, the morning mist and sunset colours, noon's bleaching glare and the cool of evening are exactly what clue us—and other animals and plants—in to the time of day. It's only in the absence of these factors that circadian rhythms reveal themselves clearly. The steady heartbeat in the background takes total charge when nothing else is making much sense. One of the first observations of circadian rhythms was focused on a mimosa plant kept in a dark cupboard in eighteenth-century France. Mimosa leaves open at dawn to catch sunlight for photosynthesis, then fold and lower at night, opening pores called stomata to respire while the air is cool enough to minimize water loss. Physician, geologist, botanist and mathematician Jean-Jacques d'Ortous de Mairan had a Renaissance man's fascination with the mechanics of everything around him, including ancient scrolls, astronomy and his mimosa plant's daily movements. The plant in his cupboard followed its time-specific activities in the absence of light. Its leaves stiffened during the day and drooped at night, just as they would in the outside world. From petal movements to fragrance release, there is a right time for everything, and the plant chugged along on its business even in the darkness.

In the early 1960s at the University of Tübingen, Germany, scientists conducted experiments holding bats in man-made dwellings and monitoring both their evening exits to feed on insects at dusk and their dawn returns to retire again for the day. Patricia DeCoursey is a pioneer in the field, having discovered the study of circadian rhythms in graduate school at the University of Wisconsin–Madison in the 1950s. Wild rodents became her specialty, and she described and analyzed their circadian rhythms throughout a distinguished career in the biological sciences department at the University of South Carolina. Her post-doctoral work in Germany involved setting up and monitoring these bat houses, which look very much like birdhouses. Providing no sunsets or cooling air to cue the bats' departure, DeCoursey showed that the lab bats still kept their nightly schedule. Presumably, it's advantageous for the bats to wake in anticipation of the arrival of the insects, which are spurred by their own tiny internal timekeepers. The external signs of dusk are less foolproof: The sky can darken from a storm, for example, or a warm front might move in at dusk, covering the natural temperature dip.

A documentary crew visited me last year in Yellowknife at the end of a long series of shoots they'd been doing around the world, including scenes at the World Trade Center site in New York, where thousands of migratory birds are trapped and die in the powerful light beams installed as a memorial. Then, after they'd captured the insanity of Toronto's nightclub district, they went to Greece to film the atmospheric rituals of a midnight mass followed by spectacular rocket displays. Now they had come to Yellowknife to see the northern lights, because we are situated directly underneath the auroral oval. They also wanted to hear from me about the circadian rhythms of nighttime.

Director Michael McNamara wrenched himself from a snow-mobile and burst into the houseboat, full of apologies. His team had already set up lights for an interview. Accompanied by a sub-zero blast of lake air and a cloud of condensation, he took off his borrowed parka, looking much more comfortable in his all-black, urban-arts-scene attire. Nothing in McNamara's director's reel hinted that he might take on a sweeping, philosophical film. I'd already seen one of his pieces, a great profile of an upstart European film company that changed Hollywood. He'd also writ-ten and directed three investigations of body-image issues—one about large-breasted women and their attitudes toward their bodies, another equivalent one on small-breasted women and, to complete the trilogy, a movie called *Penis Dementia: The Search for the Perfect Penis*. The project he'd come to see me about was on an order of magnitude more ambitious in scope and in content.

Named after a book by Christopher Dewdney—which was, in turn, named after a poem by Robert Frost—the film *Acquainted with the Night* is about the nocturnal world, and it's structured as one ideal night from sunset to sunrise. I told him that night brings with it drastic changes. The stable of animals on the prowl tends to comprise far more solitary ones, because group defences work better in the daytime. The biological world turns to senses other than vision. Though humans are largely diurnal, we share a nocturnal ancestor with all mammals, and some evolutionary holdovers still link us with the night.

Birds, reptiles, amphibians and fish all can sense light in other ways than with their eyes, in particular, through the pineal gland. Mammals, however, developed different body-clock mechanisms when they passed through a "nocturnal bottleneck," an evolu-tionary period when they were night-active.

In mammals, there is an area of the brain where many coordin-ating functions take place. The hypothalamus is a structure low in the brain that links the nervous system with the endocrine (hormonal) system, via the pituitary gland. Like a multi-function thermostat, the hypothalamus monitors and controls essential life-sustaining functions—it balances hormones and electrolytes, and it juggles fat and carbohydrate metabolism as well as sugar levels and blood pressure. Most germane to our discussion, it manages body temperature as well as sleeping and waking cycles. Within the hypothalamus is the *suprachiasmatic nucleus* (SCN), two tiny bundles of neurons, placed just above the X where the optic nerves meet and cross. The SCN is the master clock of all mammals.

Before the middle of the eighteenth century, clock time varied incrementally by locality, corresponding to local time measurements like a public sundial. It was only when railway schedules had to be coordinated with precision that standard time was introduced, forcing individual towns out of their exact solar time and into a generic block of uniform time they shared with neighbours down the line. In the same way that this allowed society to better coordinate transportation and industry, the master clock hones the body's ability to dedicate time to each biological priority. In humans, the SCN is very active in the day and inactive at night—hence the regular oscillations in motion that make it a clock—and it gets information on light levels from the eyes, calibrating its phase. In nocturnal mammals, the reverse is true, with SCN neurons firing rapidly through the night and calming in the day.

From the SCN, the output connections go to other parts of the brain to trigger hormones, which, in turn, flow through the bloodstream to calibrate peripheral internal clocks in the heart, liver, lungs and other organs. This system of multiple pacemakers is subordinated to the master clock, but when the organs are isolated, they continue to demonstrate rhythmicity. When the SCN moves to an inactive phase, melatonin, the sleepiness hormone, is free to circulate, and the body prepares for sleep. As the nucleus revs up again in the early morning, the brain stem's arousal system receives the signals and cortisol—the stress and alertness hormone—surges to help the body mobilize for waking.

Though mammals fall into both nocturnal and diurnal species, light sets the clocks for both types. If diurnal animals' eyes receive light—especially the light in the blue portion of the visible spectrum—during the time the SCN is most active, there is no effect on the clock's phase, because the day inside matches the day outside. But if there is light when the body thinks it's late evening, the SCN shifts its rhythm later, setting its clock back to accommodate the later daylight. If, on the other hand, there is light coming into the eyes during the wee hours of morning, the SCN matches its pace by advancing the phase, that is, by starting that day earlier and then finishing earlier too. How much the SCN advances or delays depends on how strong that light is and how long it lasts.

If there's any doubt about how essential these systems are to an animal's survival, just watch what happens when the SCN is removed. Ground squirrels—related to chipmunks, prairie dogs and groundhogs—look like the common squirrel but spend very little time in trees. They are a cautious tribe who stand up on their hind legs and scan for danger with the regularity common to prey animals. In keeping with her rodent specialty, Patricia DeCoursey has worked with them extensively. At night, they tend to stay safely in their dens, but when DeCoursey removed the SCN from their brains, they wandered out into the open part of their desert enclosure during all hours of the night, when they lacked the vision to protect themselves. Though not part of the experiment, a stray cat managed to break into the cage and eat a few before the experimenter could save them! In the wild, behaviour like this would have been selected against naturally and within a very few generations. Any wild ground squirrels that took to wandering

FIREFLY MAGIC

Fireflies glow only at night, even if they're kept in constant darkness for a week. It's a little bit of magic a child might discover ...

aimlessly in the night would soon suffer the evolutionary consequences and that tendency would be eliminated.

Nonmammals don't have such a centralized, coordinated system. Often small, translucent animals, such as tropical rainforest frogs, actually reset the rhythms of their peripheral organs directly by sunlight.

There is such power in the ubiquity of circadian rhythms. Through the continuous dance of light and darkness, the rotation of the Earth has become ingrained in almost all life. It connects us as fundamentally as the water we all need and the sunlight from which we all, ultimately, draw our energy. We have only just begun to grasp the implications this connectedness may have for our future and for that of all life on Earth.

TWO

from mice to men

Every year, dozens of madmen race across America on bicycles. That's 4,761 kilometres of cycling. It's called the Race Across America, bizarrely, and the winner five out of the last six years was a former Slovenian soldier named Jure Robic. Until his death in a traffic accident in 2010, he led the endurance-race scene, pushing himself to the edge of mental breakdown. He would go eight days on a total of eight hours' sleep. I am the mother of a newborn and at this very moment, Jure Robic is my personal hero. There's no snooze button on a hungry baby.

I'm groping blearily for a diaper in the dark. The race is on to swap diapers and start the baby feeding before his whining cry intensifies and he wakes himself up. Kneeling on the sheepskin that serves as my newborn son's bed, I rest my tired head on my hands and my eyelids droop as I listen to him swallowing—after every suck, at first, then every two or three. It's dark out, but I'm not going to bother looking at the clock. It'll only depress me to know how little I've slept. Oh, I sleep, all right, but in thirty-minute stretches while the baby's out for the count. A newborn's eyes are closed more often than not, after all, so it sounds like a recipe for ample rest. Trouble is, the human body is not adapted to three-hour cycles, and try as you might, you never really adjust. As any parent knows, there are times of the day when you'd simply rather be sleeping. There are others when you'd rather be awake.

We come by it honestly—it's something we share with the rest of the life forms on Earth, and possibly with those elsewhere. So as my infant son nods off mid-morning and I glance dubiously at the bedroom, it's not just the streaming daylight that prevents me from crawling under the covers. It's the confused protest from every last cell in my body. They know what time it is, and there's no fooling them.

When I first encountered circadian rhythms, I knew that here was a hidden force with a hand, biologically, in everything. Circadian rhythms in humans are no less powerful than they are in our non-human counterparts—in their ability to adapt our sleeping and waking, our eating and working, to the environmental cycle around us. They're masked only by the environments we create for ourselves using artificial light and clock technologies. Like many animals, we have an internal pacemaker that runs the show, coordinating each organ's daily cycle. Every morning when dawn brightens our faces, the SCN in our brain recalibrates itself to the original clock, whose face is the sky and whose little hand is the sun.

The perpetual darkness of winter near the north and south poles, as well as the midnight sun in summer, have attracted researchers who see these environments as natural laboratories for testing the limits of our daily rhythms. In 1955, in one such experiment, human subjects were taken up to Svalbard, a stunningly beautiful and mountainous archipelago in the Norwegian Arctic, during the midsummer season of perpetual daylight.

There, at a latitude of around 80 degrees north, two-thirds of the archipelago is covered by twenty-three nature reserves, protecting polar bears, reindeer and marine mammals. As sunny and clear as the summer day is in Svalbard, the average summer temperatures are only slightly above freezing.

The experimental subjects were given wristwatches that, unbeknownst to them, were modified to keep a twenty-seven-hour day. Over nine real days, the subjects' watches measured out only eight. The researchers monitoring their physical functions found that some parts of their bodies were deceived—but other parts knew better, keeping the real time and continuing to cycle on a twenty-four-hour timetable. Though we have conscious access to sleeping patterns, other things—like potassium excretion rates, mediated by the kidneys—are beyond our control. When body temperature and sleeping times decouple (the most common problem in jet lag), everything else is thrown out of whack. It's hard to sleep when your body temperature is elevated. Societally accepted eating times in the new zone unfortunately coincide with the internal time for slower digestion.

Some organs even adjust by taking the long route, independently shifting around the clock in the opposite direction from the others. This is possible when the central clock's signals are weakened by lack of synchronized reinforcement from the environment. Internal clocks in each of the organs are then able to function more independently. Each organ relies on its own clock while the whole system resets itself. The resulting lack of internal coordination translates into feeling groggy and ill.

Our self-awareness really sets us apart because we can mask our natural rhythms. We have the capacity to override instinctual behaviour and to bend our biology to our conscious will, at least up to a point. If we decide to go for a run in the middle of the night, our body temperature will artificially rise, masking the natural nighttime drop. As we huff and puff down the street, our breathing will accelerate to about twenty times its normal rate of air intake compared to resting levels, revving up our systems to an approximation of daytime functioning. Going to sleep is a decision we make consciously. It's a decision made easier by peer behaviour—when we see family members doing the same thing, for example, and by habit, perhaps signalled by clocks striking the bedtime hour. As the people around us shift into more sedentary activities, turning down lights, expecting quiet, we follow their cues and prepare ourselves, mentally and physically, for sleep. But the daily cycles of the internal organs aren't optional: The bladder's daytime demands, for example, are made independent of individual volition. Sleep-wake cycles are consciously determined until exhaustion sets in, but other underlying physiological processes run themselves strictly by the SCN's master clock, not consulting with the mind at all.

Down seven flights of steep stone steps and through a claustrophobic labyrinth of corridors deep beneath Munich's downtown hospital lies the Bunker. It's an old bomb shelter from the Second World War and the perfect place to find circadian oblivion. Neither sound nor light penetrates the tiny apartment's walls. In the 1950s and '60s, the Bunker became a laboratory for one of the founders of the circadian rhythms field, Jürgen Aschoff. Slightly built and bespectacled, he had a loud voice and liked to hold his pipe aloft and pontificate.

With no telephones, radios or wristwatches—just plenty of food and a few sticks of furniture—Aschoff's subjects spent a month at a time in the chamber. There was a light switch they could turn on or off whenever the mood struck, and they collected their urine for analysis and regularly took their own temperature (rectally, no less). They amused themselves with a record player and books. Never mind how atypical someone would have to be to agree to such a character-building assignment; it's clear that this was a self-selected group and hardly a cross-section of the population. Nevertheless, these studies were the first to show that humans have the same free-running cycles as the rest of the natural world.

An eight-hour period of sleeping and an active period added up to around 24.3 hours, and all the other bodily measurements cycled in synchrony. Each day, the subjects rose from their beds twenty minutes later than the day before, and by the time the month had passed, they had lost all touch with the wider world clock. The human mind is constantly acting on its own perceptions of time, taking its cues both from inside the body and from its own accounting of minutes. Of course, the clock that evolution has fashioned can only approximate the to-the-second exactitude of Earth's rotation period; still, nature works with rough tools, and under all but laboratory conditions, the circadian system keeps living beings in sync with the solar system. These days, similar studies go on in circadian isolation units that boast a little more sophistication, including video games and a television for watching movies.

Aschoff himself participated in the research, sequestering himself underground to monitor his own rhythms. He had a bunker built near the Andechs monastery in Bavaria, and his staff made sure no details were left unaccounted for, to prevent him from knowing the time. Male staff shaved their beards at random times, so he couldn't tell the time from a "five o'clock shadow" and the whole facility was surrounded in copper wire to block out any electromagnetic time cues.

Aschoff and his team did roughly a hundred and fifty such experiments, but rarely did subjects commit to more than a month's isolation. French spelunker and geologist Michel Siffre had a different idea. In 1962, at the age of twenty-three, Siffre was studying underground glaciers in the Alps. He decided to take a two-month research trip in a cave seventy kilometres from Nice, but almost on a lark, to make it interesting, he committed to living "like an animal." No watch, no clock, no calendar, but most of all, no sunlight.

This was before ethics review boards and other such cautionary measures that, nowadays, might have spoiled the adventure, likely deeming his methods unnecessarily risky and refusing him funding for his study—there were many safer ways to achieve comparable results, after all. Photos from the experiment show a heavily bearded Siffre lying on a dirty foam mattress in a tent, his scalp hooked up to a dozen wires, reading Plato. Electrodes monitored not only brainwaves, but also heart and muscle activity. His team, newly recruited for the French Institute of Speleology he had founded that year, was at the ready on the surface, waiting for him to call when he woke up, when he ate and when he went to bed—all just when he felt like it. Conditions were miserable, as one might expect. Humidity saturated the air and temperatures were consistently sub-zero. He was hypothermic at times, but he continued to read and write in his tent.

After setting up camp on July 16, Siffre planned to emerge from the cave on September 14. One day—August 20 by Siffre's count—when he reckoned he'd reached the halfway point in the experiment with one more month to go, his team called to him to celebrate the end of the experiment. Somewhere in there, Siffre had lost a month of subjective time, a difference of a factor of two. He attributes the large perturbation in his sense of time to the darkness. "I believe that when you are surrounded by night—the cave was completely dark, with just a light bulb—your memory does not capture the time. You forget," he writes. "After one or two days, you don't remember what you have done a day or two before. The only things that change are when you wake up and when you go to bed. Besides that, it's entirely black. It's like one long day."

Of course, the adventurer confirmed what the bunker experiments had suggested: Namely, he followed a twenty-four-and-a-half-hour free-running rhythm. Later he facilitated similar—and even longer—case studies on fellow speleologists. All of these subjects encountered a fascinating anomaly that seems only to happen during extended periods of unlit isolation: a forty-eight-hour day. During these episodes, twelve hours of sleep followed thirty-six continuous hours of activity, but the diary entries from these days show no awareness of their difference from a twenty-four-hour day.

This was at the height of the Cold War, when the French military had just gotten into nuclear submarines, so they funded Siffre's venture to help them predict the sleeping patterns of the members of their navy. They were also quite excited by the prospect of a thirty-six-hour day for their troops. NASA chipped in too, for all the sophisticated mathematical analyses, having yet to discover how sleep was going to work in outer space.

According to the handwritten scrawl on my birth certificate, I was born in the John Radcliffe Hospital in Oxford, England (my official name definitely starts with *J*, but the rest is open to the interpretation of autography experts). On a January morning thirty years later, I return to the hospital, hoping my meeting with one of the luminaries of chronobiology won't be scuttled by the snow that has shut down most of southern England's bus systems and made motorists overly cautious. Getting into the Nuffield ophthalmology lab is like running an orientation course, with multiple buzzings-in and much riding of elevators and waiting on couches for assistants. At the end of it all stands Dr. Russell Foster, the man who recast the science of eyes to include circadian rhythms.

Foster, an energetic and welcoming man, leads me to his office, a self-contained den set off from the newsroom-style desk complex inhabited by the rest of the staff. He apologizes for the stacks of papers and boxes waiting to be arranged on empty shelves after a recent move, and I balance my coffee on the flattest binder I can find out of those covering the nearest table. I have come to see Foster because, after a long battle with the status quo, he has shown the scientific community that ophthalmology is about more than just vision.

The eye has two distinct functions: to see and to detect light. Though these might sound like the same thing, the system for setting circadian rhythms uses light in a different way than vision does. Rods and cones are the two best-known photoreceptors, the former used for peripheral and night vision, the latter for colour vision. Foster discovered a third kind of photoreceptor, the *melanopsin ganglion*, in an inner layer of the retina. Unlike rods and cones, whose signals are precisely mapped before transmission to the vision centres of the brain, melanopsin ganglia communicate only the general brightness of the light that hits them. *Melanopsin* is the photopigment that chemically reacts to light—and to blue light in particular—and the message travels through a special nerve tract to the SCN.

Some blind people—depending on what type of damage they've sustained—are able to use this third photoreceptor to recalibrate their rhythms each day. Since Foster's discovery, surgeons working on certain eye diseases are careful to preserve an intact eye so that circadian function is not destroyed. Researchers have also discovered a link between the melanopsin photoreceptors and the light sensitivity that triggers headaches in some migraine sufferers. These are just the first of many applications that might stem from Foster's discovery.

Foster is excited to share his latest research—the subject of a public talk later in the evening on that January day—about circadian dysfunction in psychiatric diseases with strong biological bases, like schizophrenia and Alzheimer's. Not only could sleep-wake patterns help identify what damage there has been to the brain and even diagnose an illness, but addressing sleep problems themselves could be a type of early intervention against brain illness. Foster's crinkly-eyed enthusiasm is contagious.

It's easy to see how he brought a fresh perspective to the study of eyes as a sensory organ: He didn't start down the same path as the others, chomping through two hundred years of ophthalmological orthodoxy. Instead, Foster looked at the way frogs detect light for their circadian system and learned about how the reptilian pineal gland is directly light-sensitive. It wasn't a huge leap to hypothesizing that the body clock uses information about brightness separate from the regular vision system. Foster's findings have led to a different approach to ophthalmology, opening a new branch of study around the light-sensing system and its pathways.

§

They say our world is shrinking, figuratively, and a new class of global citizens straddles the borders of continents as part of its daily lifestyle. Nowhere is constant travel more universally expected than in the world of professional sports. Even at the lowest levels of participation, travel is part and parcel of competition. At the peak of human performance, the physiological effects of circadian function can make or break an athlete, so the culture of sports is adjusting more than most to this unprecedented mobility.

Having stashed my parka in the car in the Northwest Territories before I left, I'm ready for the warm November day that greets the plane in Phoenix. Palm trees line the way to Tempe, host this year to the Ford Ironman Arizona. More than two thousand participants, many of them professionals or Olympians, gather for the gruelling festival of endurance.

The race starts with a 2.4-mile swim in a lake whose water quality makes the locals shudder. Then the athletes hop onto their bikes for a 112-mile looping tour of the hilly trails around town. If they're still kicking after that, they've got a 26.2-mile run (a full-length marathon in itself) ahead of them.

The transition from cycling to running is notoriously off-putting, and much of the training centres on it. BRICK workouts, short for "Bike-Run-Ick," get the legs used to the rubbery feeling of running the last stage. At the bike-to-run change point, I watch efficient teams of volunteers grab bikes from incoming triathletes. The bib numbers are shouted out and recorded, and the bicycles—mostly high-end Cervélos—are passed back to a vast field full of them, sometimes with contestants' bike shoes still clipped to the pedals. The field's contents must be worth millions now, but there's not much security, just a complex of porta-potties.

Hawkers in nearby tents offer Hammer Gel energy syrups and salt tablets. A giant inflated sports-drink bottle marks the bleachers around the race's end, where volunteers are fooling around with the finish-line ribbon, pretending to run through it and striking a variety of victorious poses. They might as well amuse themselves: They've got a long wait for the real finishers. The fastest triathletes today will take more than eight hours to complete the course.

A lady shouts from the sidelines: "Way to go, Greg! Keep it up, Mary! All right, Frank!" I think she must be really up on the sport and its big names—until I spot the competitors' name tags. On the rest stops along the way, many of the best competitors will veer aside to drink or pee, letting their heart rates drop and their absorption rates recover at the expense of precious minutes on the clock. According to coaches, this is the wisest strategy to replicate training conditions as faithfully as possible. Triathletes often train on long highways around their homes and stop in at gas stations to top up their fluids and use the facilities. Since the best race performances are a product of identical training and race habits, the rest stops are like artificial gas stations along the way.

Good athletic performance is all about getting oxygen into the blood, where it can release energy from the glycogen stores in muscle and fat. To boost breathing, it helps to have dilated airways. All these processes are optimized in the early evening. This is when swimming-power output peaks, and the ratio between breathing and oxygen uptake is best, so it's no surprise that elite athletes break most records during this window. Peaking with body temperature, running performance shows clear circadian rhythms because strength and power come from muscle contraction—a biochemical process that speeds up with temperature. Most of us will experience this primarily in our perceptions of exertion. On an evening bike ride, we can push ourselves a little harder, breathe a little more easily and typically pedal faster and for longer.

For endurance athletes like the Ironman competitors here in Arizona, timing is different, most obviously because their work-out lasts for most of the day. The long journey is not the only reason the competition starts in the early morning, when body temperatures are low and performance suboptimal. The slow race start reduces lactate buildup in the morning, so that the athletes stay below their lactate threshold—the upper limit for sustained racing—and save their glycogen stores for the long haul ahead. Ironman athletes are at serious risk of heat stress, which is a danger not only to their health but also to their race times, so by starting from a lower baseline they can achieve more distance before they cross into a higher-than-optimal body temperature. Even so, morning starts require lots of stretching, because flexibility varies with the body clock too.

But what about the athletes who have flown into Arizona from the east coast or even Europe? The eight hours represent a daylong marathon of exertion for those from nearby California or New Mexico, but the visitors are essentially running through the night.

I can't stay until midnight to watch the last stragglers come in, but I do catch the winning female, who flies in with a time of nine hours and twenty-one minutes. It's the first Ironman victory for the Dutch professional triathlete Heleen bij de Vaate, and she's thrilled. This will qualify her for the World Championship Ironman triathlon in Hawaii next October, and she's already set a goal to make the top ten there (she does, in fact, achieve just that).

Slim and attractive with a boyish haircut, Heleen is a chemical engineer by training, like her husband and coach Rob de Hooge. In fact, her main sponsor is the large chemical company that used to employ her before she dedicated herself full time to the life of an international athlete. In a single season, she's competed in Ironman races in South Africa, Malaysia, Holland and Spain. I ask Rob how they prepare for the circadian disruptions of the time delays.

"We like to get a sense of the course in advance, so if we can afford the time, we'll spend her pre-race rest week on location," he says. They spend the week recovering from jet lag, loading up on complex carbohydrates and driving the length of the race course to gauge the lay of the land.

If they don't have that luxury, Heleen resets her clock in whatever way she can. "I have to make sure I go outside right away in the morning to get my body adjusted to the new time," she says. "But even before I leave Holland, I can simulate the dawn whenever I want. I should get one of those lamps, but for now I go in the tanning bed. I think it works, but it's hard to tell."

Many aspects of physical performance are contingent upon time of day. For an endurance sport like the Ironman, pain tolerance can make the difference between an athlete pushing through that extra distance and dropping out of a race entirely. Pain thresholds decrease to a minimum around six in the evening. On the other hand, the upswing of body temperature at that time correlates with extra strength.

To avoid the worst of a day's heat, races are generally scheduled to start in the early morning, when cortisol levels are high, releasing energy from fats and proteins in the body. Everything from blood pressure and hormone levels to heart rate is chained to the daily cycle, and the more significant forms of jet lag set each organ to recovery at difference paces, destroying the synergy among systems.

Performance in a competitive athletic event is dependent on the confluence of each bodily system functioning optimally and in synchrony. One of the most powerful parts of an Ironman competitor's environment is his or her internal state—heart rate, glucose levels, even emotions—which are partly dictated by circadian rhythms. All this to say that if it's three in the morning where the athlete came from yesterday, he or she will have to contend with a strange sensation of unfamiliarity and a foggy notion of procedures that had become automatic—and will likely be denied the victory.

Athletic performance can be better understood and optimized when viewed through the lens of human ancestral daily rhythms. It's long been recognized that the longer we are awake during the average day, the less we are physically active in the average hour, so that the total physical activity remains constant. In other words, there's a certain amount of walking our body's prepared to do in a day, and it will spread the walking out over the time it's awake—presumably an evolved energy conservation strategy for when hunting or gathering days got long. The timing of that exercise affects the body clock.

WEST IS BEST

Researchers at one of Stanford's sleep disorders clinics analyzed Monday Night Football games—with kickoffs at 9 P.M. Eastern Standard Time, no matter where they are played—over the course of twenty-five National Football League seasons. They found the west coast NFL teams had a clear advantage beyond the point spread set by Las Vegas oddsmakers. They were playing during their peak athletic performance hours of the day: According to their bodies' circadian time, it was early evening. Not only did the effect enhance the western teams' home-field advantage, it totally counteracted the home-field advantage the eastern teams might otherwise have enjoyed.

If you exercise in the late evening when your body temperature would normally be dropping, you will disrupt the surge of melatonin, blunting the release of the sleepiness hormone. This is hardly astounding since we have already learned that temperature and melatonin rise and fall in opposite patterns through the day and night. Eating a carbohydrate-rich meal causes a similar effect, raising body temperature and heart rate while impeding melatonin release, and it's generally understood to be a bad idea to load supper with sugars and starches—especially if you're hoping to fall asleep soon afterward.

A neat effect emerges, though, when you exercise during a time you would never have thought to exercise: the middle of the night. It turns out that high-intensity workouts in the middle of the night, when melatonin levels have already reached their sleep-time high, actually boost that level another 50 percent. After such a wee-hours workout, your melatonin will surge later the next evening, and your body clock will shift to a later phase—potentially useful in jet-lag adjustment too, provided your hotel has a fitness centre open that late!

The danger in dispensing advice like this, though, is that not all body clocks are created equal. The body clocks in men and women tick and tock differently. More surveyed women than men report being early birds, as opposed to night owls, and their biology supports that claim. Women's melatonin levels go up more at night and down more in the day than men's—a larger swing. Men, on the other hand, see bigger daily fluctuations in body temperature. If a man and a woman go to sleep at the same time, the woman will experience the drop in body temperature and the surge in melatonin earlier. In other words, she will fall asleep at a later biological time than the man, even though their sleep times are identical as counted by the clock.

THREE

time and tide and the unfolding seasons

An avid outdoorsman and paddler, my father frequently finds reasons to visit me up in northern Canada. He's tackled the Mountain River and the Burnside, and we've paddled the Thelon River through a giant muskox sanctuary (without seeing any muskox). Arctic terns, all manner of eagles, plenty of wolves and a handful of grizzly bears make the otherwise daunting tundra landscape more companionable. If the water's not too silty, he might catch a grayling or the ultimate prize: Arctic char. He always comes back with a camera half full of tundra wildflower photos and very little evidence of his fellow travellers.

Last summer, though, Dad really hit the wildlife jackpot. There were maybe nine or ten campers in the group, with two young wilderness guides leading the way down the Coppermine River toward the community of Kugluktuk in Coronation Gulf. As the river's name suggests, nuggets of copper can be plucked off its banks and have been used for tools by Inuit for hundreds of years. Dad's paddling partner was a retired Colorado engineer named Terry, who had shared our Thelon River adventure three years earlier. Terry's passion was film and photography. Watching his DVD footage from the trip, I see the guides horsing around with the camera after their charges have gone to sleep. Then there's a shot of my father, woken in the middle of the sun-bathed Arctic night, standing on a rock in his blue cotton pajamas, mouth agape. The river next to his campsite is filled with caribou. They are leaping from rock to rock in front of him—thousands upon thousands upon thousands of them. Travelling for thousands of kilometres, caribou from the Northwest Territories and Nunavut—estimated at over a million animals—perform the longest overland migration of any animal in the world. From their winter foraging grounds below the treeline to their tundra calving grounds in the Arctic, the animals run for long hours, pursued by wolves and eagles that target the calves. They clock in at a pace of well over sixty kilometres per hour. The hollow winter hair on their backs keeps them afloat as they bob across the water, spindly legs pumping. Their summer eyes flash yellow, transformed from their winter deep blue so as to block out the light most likely to reset their circadian systems. Next to Dad's beached canoe and stored life jacket, the little ones clamber onto the shore with their mums, and the bulls haul their heavy antlers with purpose.

Being caught up in a caribou migration is any Arctic adventurer's dream, and it's becoming less likely every year as the population crashes. In the last decade alone, caribou counts have been decimated, and no one quite knows what to blame. To reverse the trend, hunting bans were tried, but the local communities responsible for managing the caribou protested not only that it would jeopardize their traditional way of life, but also that their hunting was a negligible influence on the vast herds. Another concern is *trophic mismatch*: the plants that pregnant caribou depend on during calving season are reaching their peak nutritional value earlier as spring thaws happen earlier due to climate change. Caribou don't time their breeding to temperature, however; they reach their calving grounds at the same month each year according to day length. There they find their food already past its prime, meaning their calves are less likely to survive, and both mother and offspring will be undernourished and unprepared for the migration ahead. Nevertheless, the great caribou migration remains one of nature's most spectacular annual phenomena.

This yearly event is caused by rhythms that are internally generated and rule a species' existence, but that don't fit the term *circadian rhythms* because they don't relate to the solar day. Migration, reproduction and hibernation often run on a yearly schedule and sometimes on an even longer cycle—take the cicada's thirteen- or seventeen-year-long rhythms, for example. But even without all the clues an animal might have as to the calendar date (day length and temperature, primarily), the urge to migrate will still arise once a year, drifting slightly as the years pass because, after all, calendar accuracy is a tall order for a bird (or caribou) brain. Seasonality is all part of the body clock's package, especially the nearer a creature is to the poles.

Just as nature pulses on a daily tempo, it also counts out the seasons—and sometimes the years. For a Canada goose to prepare himself for spring migration, he needs considerable lead time to fatten up. He'll also moult his winter feathers and grow his gonads for mating season. Light-sensitive parts of his brain sense the sun's rays through the top of his skull and measure the length of each day. As he becomes aware of the increasing daylight hours—calculated using his circadian clock—his hormones respond with seasonally appropriate behaviour. Assuming he isn't one of the geese that have taken up permanent residence in a human habitat, switching his diet to year-round agricultural produce and enjoying safety from predators (obviating the need for migration), he will travel the route he was shown as a gosling, year after year.

Some seasonal changes are cued by temperature, whereas others are scheduled by day length—known as *photoperiod*—and still others are governed by an internal clock that takes roughly a year to complete each cycle. We still have no idea where this clock is housed, if anywhere, or how it works, but the evidence for its existence is strong.

One advantage caribou have, along with their avian Arctic compatriot the ptarmigan, is the ability to flatten their melatonin cycles. Melatonin is a hormone synthesized in the brain's pineal gland—once thought to be the seat of the soul. The level of melatonin in the blood rises to induce and sustain sleep and then falls during waking hours in a daily cycle under the control of the SCN. In day-active animals, exposure to melatonin has the sleep-promoting effects of a period of sustained darkness. In fact, the circadian system's reaction to darkness is to release melatonin, suggesting that this is the mechanism by which the SCN translates light levels into bodily responses. Because caribou spend a certain amount of time in a landscape of twenty-four-hour sun, their internal clock isn't regulated by a twelve-hour melatonin low (the impetus for an active day) and a sleepy twelve hours of high melatonin levels: Caribou respond to perpetual daylight with a suspension of their circadian rhythms. This means that their energy levels remain high, regardless of the time of day, increasing their ability to forage whenever the opportunity arises. They become arrhythmic, with seemingly random bursts of energy as they charge en masse toward new pastures or away from the scent of a predator.

Birds that migrate from east to west or from west to east suspend their body clock's activities as well, but their reason for damping down their rhythms is to combat jet lag. When they release the inhibitions on their body clocks again, after a long flight across time zones, their clocks set to local time right away. Even north-to-south migrators do this to some extent so that when the day length changes with latitude, it doesn't confuse their circadian systems into making constant adjustments.

The biologists who demonstrated the existence of yearly, or *circannual*, rhythm are true heroes of the scientific process. They are the long-distance runners of the scientific universe. A three-week experiment for a circadian rhythms researcher would become a twenty-one-year project for a scientist studying circannual rhythms trying to establish the same number of data points. Circannual studies are comparable, in a way, to the rare longitudinal psychology studies that follow human subjects for a lifetime, testing them at various ages to see how they are developing and changing—and bringing to light many secrets of lifelong health and happiness. And, like those studies, circannual projects reveal richly rewarding big-picture knowledge.

Canadian biologist Ted Pengelley and German ornithologist Eberhard Gwinner were pioneers of the circannual rhythms field who focused their attentions on stonechats—robin-sized birds native to the United Kingdom and whose call sounds like two stones being tapped together. Pengelley and Gwinner showed free-running circannual reproduction in the birds; that is, they will carry on breeding on an annual cycle even in the absence of real-world cues. The scientists also demonstrated circannual rhythms in ground squirrel hibernation for up to ten years in a row. By manipulating the conditions in which the animals lived for so many years, they were able to gather clues to how internal circannual rhythms might work.

Gwinner put European starlings on a regimen of twenty-two-hour days, with eleven hours of light followed by eleven hours of darkness. The birds adapted to the altered day–night cycle, changing their testis size every ten months, where their outside-world counterparts waited twelve months. Evidence so far suggests the circannual clock can also work without real-world cues, just like the circadian clock. Just as light calibrates the twenty-four-hour cycle, day length causes the annual clock to reset, confirm and fine-tune its timing. In fact, when an animal moults, fattens up, changes its gonad size and migrates, each of these processes will free run with slightly different periods. In contrast to circadian rhythms, which are centralized in the SCN for mammals and in the pineal gland for birds, it looks like circannual clocks are myriad and decentralized.

The circannual system also runs independently of the circadian system—it's not always about counting off 365 clock-measured days. The uncanny ability to estimate periods of an entire year, repeatedly, is prominent among the longer-lived migratory species that travel long distances through many latitudes. These particular species need to rely on something even steadier than day length, unlike most other animals, for whom day length is a sufficient indicator of the time of year. As a species travels in a long-distance migration, day length changes in a way that doesn't indicate the seasons, and day length doesn't change nearly enough in the tropics, where the creatures need to time their

THE FLIGHT OF THE BUTTERFLY

North America's archetypal butterfly, the monarch, undertakes one of the most famous cross-continent migrations every year—from Canada to Mexico and back again. It's all the more remarkable when the insect's small size and short lifespan are taken into account. Four generations—each one passing from long, ridged eggs to black, white and yellow caterpillars, through a blue-green chrysalis and into the iconic orange-and-black adult stage—are involved in each yearly cycle. Though no individual insect makes the full round trip, the population as a whole mimics the north-to-south migration of birds: The monarch is the only species of butterfly to do so.

departures. Biology found a more reliable calendar by developing it within the body, though where in the body it is and exactly how it works, we have no idea. The whole year is somehow estimated internally, even when no real-world seasonal cues are available. In this day and age, to have something so fundamental be totally unknown ... it's enough to keep a biologist gleefully working late into the night.

🕭

Rhythm cycles shorter than a day also coexist internally alongside circadian rhythms in some coastal creatures. Crabs, for example, that skitter behind the surf and snap up goodies left on the shore are attuned to the ocean's complex tidal cycle. As the moon waxes and wanes, the high and low tides turn at varying times, and the shoreline's erratic dance requires a nautical almanac—or a fisherman's knowledge—to predict. The crab's behaviour evolved so that it could find safety at times of day when it is most vulnerable, while making use of scavenging opportunities as soon as its food drifts in on the tide. Survival at the ocean's margins is a kind

WANDERING PENGUINS

Penguins in the Antarctic use the sun to navigate, and as the sun in summer is constantly circling the sky, they have to use their body clocks to translate time and sun position into direction. Kidnap a penguin from his rookery and place him out on the snow, and he will waddle north until he gets to the sea—a handy rule of thumb whenever you are near Antarctic shores. Once at the coast, he can find his way home under water. On cloudy days, though, he will wander aimlessly. Releasing him six time zones away, however, which on Antarctica is not such a far hike, will cause him to waddle directly west, befuddled by his jet lag.

of arbitrage—a negotiation between water and land that requires precision timing.

Take a horseshoe crab out of the ocean and drive her many miles to a laboratory across the continent, and she will behave as if she never left home. Given a sloping surface in her cage, the crab will scrabble uphill at the same time as the water is climbing the banks of her native marine habitat back at the ocean. She will bound down again when the water's flow has reversed, then make the necessary adjustments and hit the marks for high and low tide as accurately as if she were drawing on a nautical almanac. It will be several months before circadian drift takes her off course and she loses touch with the rhythms of the sea.

The mouse, the rat and the fruit fly seem to get all the glory in biology. As the archetype of mammalian biology, mice are used to test all manner of substances for eventual human consumption. They're easily bred in large numbers from strictly controlled strains and the individuals from these breeding colonies are nearly identical, which means that the effects emerging from studies are likely the result of experimental manipulations rather than individual differences. Considering how externally different from humans they appear, it is frankly amazing how similar their responses to stimuli—even the psychological effects they show—often prove to be. The frequent congruence of mouse and human responses leads many rodent researchers to conclude that the difference in human and rodent experience or consciousness is one of degree, not of kind. Clearly this has ethical implications, not least of which concerns the research these scientists are conducting. If rodents share the same sort of pain and distress that humans are capable of, they should be treated with comparable care. The ethical implications of experiments on fruit flies are perhaps less of a challenge, and the flies are no less useful. If mice and rats are indispensable as models of human behaviour, then the fruit fly remains invaluable for studies of multi-generational effects. Their lifespan is short and they breed like crazy, so the effects of natural selection and Mendelian genetics (Gregor Mendel being the enterprising monk whose experiments on peas we all remember from high school) can be directly observed, demonstrating Darwinian principles of evolution.

Another biological model that's been inexplicably overlooked in the popular media is the thale cress plant—a tiny off-white flower native to Asia, Europe and Northwest Africa. Thale cress has been equally useful in the study of plants, because of its short life cycle (six weeks), small genome, easy cultivation and abundant seeds. It's such an old standby for botanists that its genome was the first plant genome ever to be fully sequenced—in 2000, to help with research. Principles of flower development and light sensing have been largely derived from thale cress specimens. How plants avoid the shade (to maximize energy input from the sun), germinate and—our current subject—practise *photoperiodism* (responding to the seasons by sensing the changing day length) have all been elucidated through experimentation on this tiny flowering plant.

Andrew Millar of the University of Edinburgh puts luciferase, the stuff fireflies glow with at night, into the very fabric of these plants. Luciferase is an enzyme that emits light—in this case, a greenish glow—when chemically reacting with its counterpart luciferin. After genetically inserting luciferase reporter genes linked to the circadian system, Millar and his colleagues spray the thale cress with luciferin, which activates the glow. The thale cress glows brighter and brighter until its subjective noon, when it slowly goes dim again into its night. Fireflies are nocturnal, and they glow in the dark, when they are most active. Likewise, the thale cress activates its luciferase in its most active period, the day.

By placing a video camera in a dark cupboard full of these glowing plants, Millar can visually detect when their circadian systems are most active. Then he can manipulate various environmental factors and measure the effects on the plant's internal clock. It's a lot easier than trying to measure leaves' daily stiffening (as de Mairan did in the eighteenth century) to gauge circadian functioning. From these experiments, we've learned that about a quarter of the thale cress's genes are linked to the circadian system.

Changing photoperiod as a seasonal cue for plants to flower isn't actually detected through the length of the day, but rather of the night—a distinction that adds up to the same thing, but suggests a different mechanism. Light signals are collected by mature leaves, which absorb violet and red light but reflect green light off their chlorophyll. Photoreceptor proteins detect either red- or blue-spectrum light. But the light's duration is not counted off through the hours of the day to determine day length. It's not how *many* hours of light there are that matters, but *when* in the course of a twenty-four-hour cycle the light strikes the leaves. If the sunlight arrives in the late evening, even for a few minutes, the plant behaves as though the day is longer (in the case of a spring flower, it'll get ready to bloom). Light during a critical hour (say, seven o'clock in the evening) triggers the first steps toward flowering.

So it's the period of uninterrupted darkness the plant is actually measuring. An hour of darkness in the middle of the day has no effect on when the plant flowers. In fact, if the plant is given light only at dawn, to keep its clock set, and then once more in the late evening, it will still behave as if it had been bathed in sunlight all the time in between.

The first flowering plants grew in tropical environments, where day length didn't vary much. Rather than flowering according to photoperiod, they flowered when they reached a certain developmental stage or age. Photoperiodism evolved later, when flowering plants spread to the temperate regions, and then the evolutionary innovation caught on in the tropics as well. Plants closer to the tropics are usually prompted to flower by short days (late in the summer after the solstice), whereas the temperate and polar regions have a lot of flowers that bloom in spring and early summer, activated by longer stretches of daylight.

As a safety mechanism to protect them against freak weather events, plants often have temperature thresholds that veto seasonal changes even if the day length is right. Plants do not have an internal thermostat as such. Rather, they sense temperature through the internal processes that are already affected by temperature, like the fluidity of their membranes, the speed of their metabolic processes and the shape of their proteins. After flowering, a lot of plants need a prolonged cold period—sometimes forty days in a row—before they are sensitive to day length again, ensuring they don't flower twice in one season. Of course they're still measuring day length for reasons other than flowering, like the impending doom of winter's cold—the number one killer of both plants and animals. Shorter days lead plants to stop growing, and then when the first frost hits they're ready to harden as a way to acclimatize to winter. Alternately, they store nutrients underground in tubers or bulbs, sacrificing the visible part of the plant, which they'll regrow come spring.

In the fall, when the days get shorter, deciduous trees shunt energy out of their leaves and abandon them, sending everything that matters into their roots and trunk. They use a combination of cooling temperatures and day length to trigger their winter adaptation, and they can even sense the decrease in the intensity of daylight as the hemisphere tilts away from direct overhead sun exposure. Light-absorbing molecules—called phytochromes—within the leaves take a number of forms that each respond to a different wavelength of light. As slanted light goes through more atmosphere before it reaches the Earth, its wavelength changes enough for the plant to detect. For some seasonal plant responses, the critical threshold for light intensity is linked to some wavelengths more than others.

Evergreens keep their leaves—or needles—which are built to conserve water, because they can't extract water from the soil or rainfall during much of winter. Water that's frozen is inaccessible to trees, so they keep what they have locked up in the trunk and roots, mixed into a syrupy sap with a lower freezing temperature than that of pure water. Even so, if the cold is extreme enough, the sap will freeze. Wherever that happens, on the northern edge of the taiga forests, where permafrost prevents roots from taking hold, or toward the top of a mountain where the microclimate is colder, the treeline is aptly named. After some scruffy, stunted bushes, one suddenly finds nothing but low-lying shrubs above these borders.

There's a reason you find a different flower in bloom every week or two throughout the thawed seasons worldwide: Blossoming requires nutrients and resources best taken up when they're not in hot demand, so plants find their time niche and stick to it. This also helps them to synchronize with others of the same species so bees and other vectors are able to cross-pollinate them. So as not to be fooled by an early flash of hot weather, the plants wait until the day length has reached a critical point, sensitive to either increasing (for plants that bloom before solstice) or decreasing (for late-summer flowers) length.

☃

Animals adhere to seasonal rhythms as well, though their changes often go beyond the biological realm and into the behavioural. The first pet my family ever had was a tortoise the size of a Kleenex box. The term *pet* is probably less apt than, say, *garden guest*, as we never took it inside or really restricted its movements. Our happy years of companionship began when the tortoise randomly

wandered onto our front lawn. It turned out to belong to someone down the street, but they kindly handed it over to our care.
Originally baptized Agnes, the reptile was eventually found to
be male and for continuity renamed a similar-sounding Magnus.
Wisely retreating into his shell when we children were paying him
too much attention, Magnus could sometimes be coaxed out with
a buttercup. His tiny pink tongue would emerge, rewarding our
efforts by scooping up the shiny yellow flower, his favourite food.

I think my father may have hibernated Magnus in a box in the
garage once or twice, but most of the time Magnus just disappeared
of his own accord one day in late autumn and then shuffled back
into view when the worst of the cold was over. One spring, when
Magnus had been a no-show, my brother was helping to loosen the
soil in a flower bed and was horrified to discover a dead tortoise at
the end of his gardening fork. Magnus had buried himself under
the earth to hibernate, but either had failed to dig deep enough
to avoid the frost or—most likely—had starved when he ran
out of stored energy. A large proportion of hibernating animals
each year die after they burn through their food reserves too
quickly. Though many animals enter torpid states or dormancy
to conserve energy in winter, only true hibernation is dictated by
the circannual clock rather than temperature cues. Little-known
fact: Bears, the mascots of hibernation, don't actually hibernate.
It's not enough to hole up for the winter to be considered a true
hibernator. Animals that really hibernate specialize in a kind of
adaptive hypothermia that brings their body temperature down to
the point of near death. Their hearts beat at a bare-minimum rate,
and their breathing slows radically. It would not be unusual for a
chipmunk, whose heart beats one hundred and twenty times per
minute and who breathes ninety times per minute, to hibernate
with a heart rate of just five beats per minute, taking only one
breath every minute or so. Next to these specialized hibernators,
the torpor and slowed metabolism of a bear in her winter den
cannot compare.

Just as plants switch off their flowering capability after they've bloomed, only to be reset by long stretches of continuous cold, animals with specific breeding times have various ways to prevent conceiving after the prescribed month. This is important for species like hamsters that breed in spring when they're finally exposed to light in the evening. After mating, they're still receiving that light signal through the summer, so for the good of their young (and of their own health) their entire reproductive cycle collapses, and the males' gonads regress. Then the short days of autumn reset the system so it's ready for the following spring. For autumn-breeding species like sheep, the opposite occurs: Long day lengths put a damper on their reproductive system. By the fall, though, the light signals in the evening start losing their potent effect as the sheep's system becomes desensitized.

Consider the fact that day length in a particular place has always been a fair shorthand for temperature. Plants and animals evolved little stars on their internal calendars: "May 21, get ready to swim out to the place where the algae blooms." "September 2, send out some mating calls to see if there are any ladies around yet." "November 14, dig a hole and crawl into it."

The fittest young are the ones that have plenty to eat as soon as they arrive, so animals in the ocean, on land and in the air all time their births to intersect with peak food season. Tender spring grass shoots are perfect for baby herbivores, and the predators of those babies tend to be born just in time for the proliferation of their prey: Chicks are hatched when earthworms are closest to the surface of the moist soil, and falcon chicks emerge just when migrating song-birds are available to nourish them in their rapid growth.

Of course, a glut of food can't be the trigger for reproduction— fertilization has to happen long before the feast begins. So in anticipation of nature's yearly bounty, birds monitor day length, then time their breeding with the date programmed on their internal calendar. Their lightweight and translucent skulls let in light, which is detected by a photosensitive part of their brains. So, even blind birds can act on seasonal changes in day length, using the tops of their brains. Mammals, with their thick, hardy skulls and fur or hair, no longer have the benefit of this conveniently direct system. Instead, evolution has fitted them with optic systems to "see" light levels instead, at the same time as they're seeing the world visually.

Non-equatorial animals, the ones that deal with dramatic seasonal changes, almost always reserve breeding for a specific time of year and use day length to calculate their cycle. Even in the tropics, there is often a narrowly coordinated breeding time. It's still advantageous for young to emerge en masse, because predators can eat only so much at one time. As day length is complex and not drastically varied there, tropical species use rainfall or the lushness of greenery to trigger their reproduction.

Farmers and other animal specialists take advantage of their knowledge of circannual cycles to manipulate reproduction. Breeders light their horses' stalls to make mares, who would normally conceive in spring, start the process earlier, in February. This leads to births in January of the next year, making "one-year-old" horses that are the best developed of the year's crop, so more likely to win races in their class. The light at night tricks the mares' systems into thinking winter is over.

If a sheep farmer wanted to double his yearly lamb numbers, he could manipulate the day length change to move twice as rapidly through the simulated seasons. That way the sheep would experience two cycles every year instead of one, doubling the meat supply. Similarly, chicken farmers are always looking for ways to increase egg production, and if they light their chickens' coops during the night they can achieve it; in fact, they've been using this technique for hundreds of years!

One ramification scientists monitoring climate change worry about is that, while the date and day length remain unchanged, warmer temperatures in regions that were typically colder have the effect of advancing the season. Plants spring to life earlier in the year. Over the past thirty years, plant species worldwide have advanced their leafing, flowering and fruiting dates by a few days every decade, in response to temperature changes. Animals that precisely time their reproductive cycles to exploit peak feeding season are missing these windows and starving.

One example is in the simple food web of an oak tree, a winter moth and a great tit bird. Marcel Visser, Professor of Seasonal Timing of Behaviour at Groningen University, has dedicated much of his career to this system and its fine-tuned timing. Spring comes and the new oak leaves are bursting from their buds. A winter moth's eggs hatch, producing caterpillars that voraciously consume the leaves and start to fatten up. The caterpillars will starve if they hatch much before the leaves appear, but if they wait too long the tannin concentrations in the oak leaves will be high enough to make them inedible, starving the caterpillar.

The great tit lays its eggs around this time, and they hatch as the caterpillars are all plump. The great tit chick is ready to grow. Its early life stage demands the most food right when there's a glut of caterpillars to feed it. All good so far.

Trouble is, the past twenty years have seen higher temperatures, leading to an earlier bud burst. The caterpillars have adjusted their hatching to compensate, but the great tit has not. Nutritional stress—not enough to eat—on the majority of birds that are hatching too late for the feast means the great tits are headed for a population crash. Even the species that do adjust to such changes can do so only within limits. It's too short a time frame for evolution to act on, and the caterpillar peak is not the only seasonal target the bird must hit: Reproduction and feeding is a delicate dance among all kinds of seasonal events.

Food web disconnects get even more complex in the oceans, where up to thirty species can be dependent on one another, all interacting in a system. As if climate change needed another layer of complexity, scientists working to understand the effects of global change in coming years will have to learn a lot more about biological rhythms.

As fascinating as circadian and circannual rhythms research is in its own right, what makes it truly exciting to most of us is its application to humans. We all share these rhythms within us, and it turns out they have a profound effect on our lives.

5

While humans don't, as a species, migrate, moult or hibernate, they are subtly affected, biologically, by the changing seasons. Even in modern life, with seasonal weather fluctuations dulled by indoor heating and air conditioning, you are still not immune to the yearly cycles around you. Your season of birth, for example, can rig the game—albeit only slightly—for or against you in many areas of life. Research on birth month has uncovered some reliable effects. Winter birth is overrepresented in Crohn's disease sufferers and novelty-seekers. Even left- and right-handedness occurs in different proportions among winter- and summer-born children.

Once the purview of astrologers, birth-month effects (where records provide a large enough sample size) are now under statistical scrutiny. The resulting correlations, however, do not provide ready explanations. They show variation according to birth month without offering an explanation of *how* being born in a certain month makes a difference. Sunlight, temperature, prenatal nutrition—any number of factors could account for the effects we see. North Americans and Europeans born in February and

March are 10 percent more likely to suffer from schizophrenia during their lifetimes than those born in August and September. Theories about influenza exposure or prenatal vitamin D levels float around, but the truth is, we don't understand it. As confirmation of seasonal causation, we find the opposite pattern—six months shifted—for people living in the southern hemisphere.

Birth month in a calendar sense is not, strictly speaking, the variable in question; rather, the phase of the seasons seems to be the important factor. This becomes significant when we compare populations in the northern hemisphere to those in the south, where seasons are reversed within the calendar.

Danish and Austrian health records reveal clear effects of birth month on lifespan. Birth during the second quarter of the year leads, on average, to death 226 days before those born in the fourth quarter, who have the longest lifespan—provided they live past the age of fifty. Americans with autumn birthdays live fully 160 days longer, on average, than spring-born Americans, and each birth month carries its own risk assessments for various diseases, from multiple sclerosis to diabetes.

September is harvest time in Quebec's Saguenay region, and a study of birth records from the 1800s shows that being conceived at this time of plenty made a woman fitter, in the Darwinian sense. The women conceived in September and born in June had, on average, seven more grandchildren than those born in October. They achieved this by getting married earlier, "enjoying" a longer reproductive lifespan (researchers did not interview the women to determine how they felt about having giant families) and raising children who did the same. With food abundant at the beginning of pregnancy, the Quebecers could fatten up for a healthy birth.

The studies that produce these correlations are as rock-solid as any, but the conclusions to be drawn from these clear and significant correlations are anyone's guess. The *what* is established, but the *why* is still speculation.

FOUR

our ancestral rhythms

Though our earliest ancestors lived around the tropics in a fairly constant environment from month to month, the rise of modern humans parallels our move to higher latitudes with more seasonality. Biological evolution selected for features that helped us deal with the changing seasons, and cultural evolution gave us the specific behavioural strategies to cope.

In the tropical rainforest, if the tree you're sitting under isn't producing fruit, the next one probably is: There is abundance. This is where the story starts, but before long, hominids moved into the margins of the forest, where there's a slight dry season when shoots and leaves are all there is to eat. The woodlands and savannah, marked by even more drastic seasonal variation, were still more challenging environments in which to feed the family, and soon hunting trumped fruit-picking.

Still, the real seasonal challenge began 1.8 million years ago when *Homo erectus* travelled into Europe and Asia from Africa. It's around this time that the changes we see in the archaeological record coincide with the seasonality of our genus's range. Our big brains were strongly selected to enable us to adopt survival strategies. Cold winters along with migrating prey and the complex rituals needed to tackle them required more computing power than our fruit-eating predecessors needed or possessed. For a nomadic people who travel seasonally, it was an advantage to have the foresight to plan for times of rest while in an active phase—in other words, to plan for winter during summer. It takes a particularly savvy hominid to continue lugging around carefully crafted winter clothing even when it's been stinking hot for the past couple of months.

Fire is a must-have element anywhere with a significant winter. Once early humans learned to control it and to communicate that skill to the younger generations through culture, they could live in caves at higher latitudes. The light from their fires gave them access to deep tunnels within the caves and warmed their otherwise chillingly damp refuge. When they built a fire at a cave's entrance, they made for themselves a uniquely controllable space, protected from predators at the only possible access point.

Organized hunting on the open steppes involved getting together with the guys—related or not—setting up a play-by-play and communicating the game plan. They had to set up a time and place where the animals would likely be found. Coordinating different roles (I'll chase the animal and, when it turns away from the water, you ambush it from behind this rock) required them to imagine the hunt beforehand.

The transition from early to modern human involved brain enlargement. Specifically, it meant growth in the cortex (the outermost layer of brain tissue) and most especially in the prefrontal cortex, which is involved in planning, visualization of hypothetical outcomes and general foresight. This is exactly the change that enabled migration to the higher latitudes, where anticipating seasonal changes required intelligence. Animals migrate in these areas of the world and, to catch them, you have to know where they'll be and when. It was all a lot more involved than sitting on a branch picking fruit, but it was also more efficient. Catch the salmon run, and the resulting dried fish would last for months.

Predictable, rhythmic change in animal movements lends itself to further efficiency measures. Why hunt individual animals—at close range and great risk—when you can slaughter an entire herd of reindeer as they run across the steppes in their annual migration? The trick is to be waiting to intercept them at their exact point of passage—and to know where that point is, out of all the possible places to wait on the vast expanse of plains. That's the part that takes brains. Our very perception of time, a signature human achievement, may well have come out of seasonal predictions such as these.

Reproduction also runs in sync with feeding opportunity. At the wrong time in gestation, malnutrition can be catastrophic. At the very least it is likely to adversely affect the fitness of the offspring. This has been demonstrated in humans: During the Dutch famine of the mid-1940s, the war deprived tens of thousands of civilians of sustenance, and thousands starved to death. The babies exposed to famine in utero were, not surprisingly, underweight. More remarkable, the females of that group went on to produce underweight babies of their own, even at a time when food was available. It seems their bodies had been hard-wired prenatally to conserve energy for themselves. In keeping with the Earth's seasonal bounty, humans do show a residual reproductive rhythm, however muted by industrial society. Men's reproductive hormones peak in June and dip in August, and contraceptive sales and sexually transmitted diseases show a comparable seasonal trend.

The human body manages to keep track of the seasons in the same way that other mammals do—it quietly measures changes in day length. Our reproductive systems aren't directly in touch with our eyes as they take in summer light, however. They hear about the change indirectly, through our melatonin levels. As there's virtually no melatonin circulating in our blood during the day, the body clock takes note of how long melatonin is infused at night. At dusk, when the SCN stops receiving sunlight, it damps down its activity to almost nothing, which releases the pineal gland from its prohibition against melatonin infusion. The master clock remains in muted signalling mode until dawn, when it fires back up again, cutting off melatonin supply. A long infusion usually means it's winter—in a natural setting, anyway. Even if the light environment is telling a different story during an experiment, melatonin infusions are the body's preferred messenger of the seasons.

Even though the length of night—and of melatonin release—is always changing in non-equatorial places, the master clock will remember day length when it's cut out of the brain. Experiments have shown that the master clock—a little clump of neurons—will free-run on its roughly twenty-four-hour cycle in a petri dish on the countertop of a lab, quieting its activity at a time that's seasonally appropriate for dusk.

⏰

Behaviour doesn't fossilize well, particularly low-tech behaviours like sleeping. Still, anthropologists have been able to glean a little about ancestral sleeping patterns through the archaeological record, beginning in Neolithic dwelling sites and present-day traditional societies. Naked apes like us, with little tree-climbing ability, are vulnerable to a variety of dangers during sleep. It's thought that tool use and fire, as well as tightly bonded social groups, might have co-evolved to compensate for the lack of security.

When sleeping locations are out in the open, either regularly or as part of an excursion, fire takes the place of shelter. The flicker of a crackling fire is famously a soothing presence, providing warmth and smoky protection from mosquitoes and the malaria that sometimes accompanies them. The light cast by its glow allows the nearby sleeper to be reassured in a quick glance that nothing major is amiss. A whole night of fire-tending has its challenges, however, as I discover in a winter wilderness course.

Designed for Northern workers—biologists, geologists and inspectors who work in remote areas—Arctic Response's treeline survival course is a weekend out in the shivering subarctic elements. I'm here to discover what it would be like to be a prehistoric human in a harsh environment, adapting to the exposure and, above all, sleeping out among the elements. The lakes are frozen solid and the snow lies deep as we tromp into the sparse woods to see if we're equal to the task of outwitting death. The mercury is squatting well below minus 40 (Celsius or Fahrenheit: at this temperature, it's all the same). Instructor Mike Rarog has prepared a series of training exercises to simulate surviving a bush-plane crash, both south and north of the treeline. Environment Canada has sent up a manager from Calgary who is field testing the government satellite-phone call-in process. Also participating are two nurses from the air-ambulance service that shuttles patients to and from remote Northern communities.

Rarog lets us in on a secret: The survival kits on Northern bush planes—the standard mode of transport around here—are equipped with a flimsy tent that's probably never been opened, let alone tested. Furthermore, the pilots haven't undergone survival training—he's been begging them to take a course, but they don't see it as a priority. "As a paratrooper, I've boarded in Edmonton at 7 degrees [Celsius] with fully operational equipment," he says. "By the time I parachuted into Gjoa Haven [Nunavut] at minus 50, nothing works anymore." Anything with batteries dies, anything plastic cracks and crumbles. Hence our first labour-intensive and time-consuming task: constructing a lean-to for the first night, on the assumption that even if we have a tent, it's not built to withstand these temperatures.

Rarog has seen the aftermath of dozens of plane crashes. Originally a military man, he spent his early thirties doing international aid work in conflict zones and accruing valuable time at emergency scenes. When he came to Yellowknife in 1998, he began working with the air force's 440 Squadron on an in-house search-and-rescue system for its pilots. He's just back from a couple of years away from home, removing land mines in Iraq. The fifty-year-old has witnessed countless dead bodies, and his students hang on his words with morbid fascination. In the North, he's made fourteen body recoveries—many of them frozen—and, tragically, fewer saves. Rarog's training company, Arctic Response, grew to encompass occupational health and safety and curriculum development. Communities approach him to help with their emergency plans and evacuation procedures. With enough work for six full-time employees—one administrative assistant and the rest field instructors—his civilian business has picked up and eclipsed the need for military work.

Far from Tom Hanks's *Cast Away* scenario, says Rarog, long weeks of exposure are not the primary threat to people lost in the North. "Of the exposure victims who die, 50 percent are already dead within the first twenty-four hours, and 75 percent within seventy-two hours. They just shut down mentally, and it's all over." Nevertheless, he insists the human animal is at its most noble at the height of an emergency. People will regularly make enormous sacrifices for total strangers under these circumstances.

The Royal Canadian Mounted Police's search-and-rescue protocol is based on a profiling system. According to the statistics, a hunter will be found heading downhill 83 percent of the time; in contrast, a "despondent"—someone depressed after a marital breakup, for example—is likely to be sitting on a prominent outcrop, a high point of land where he or she can survey the scenery. Children under three years old have no concept of being lost, and they may be in or under objects, perhaps asleep. Officers have to keep in mind that six-to-twelve-year-olds in the woods might be sulking and may not respond to their names being called—some younger kids have admitted they thought searchers were monsters. And when a man is not found at the hunting cabin he told his wife he'd be at, one of the first RCMP processes undertaken is what's called "the bastard search." The man is often found at a motel or house with another woman.

All theory aside, though, I'm looking to gain practical experience from this most primal of scenarios, with extreme temperature added in for good measure. That's what I'm here for. As the sun begins to set on the first afternoon, my class is informed that we each have a broken arm. We must help each other splint and sling up the bad arm using whatever's at hand. Then we must work as a team—a band of one-armed plane-crash victims—to erect a simple A-frame tent. The results are hilarious, and before long, some of us are cheating, grabbing tent corners between the fingers of our supposedly immobilized hands.

Then, the effort to signal for help—two whistle blows means there's a plane overhead. There isn't, of course, but we must be ready with our pumpkin-orange tarps—ready to run around on the snow-covered lake, waving our arms and shouting. Ready to realize how small we must appear to even a low-flying pilot. As darkness takes over, we shoot off deafening signal flares that send bright pink fire across a dim showing of the northern lights. The city's airport authority has been notified in advance of the exercise. They ignore the fireworks display.

It's a non-stop barrage of survival scenarios. As we knock over dead trees to construct our temporary shelters, we're warned about placement of the shelters—crashed planes are chock full of danger. Fuel and debris will slide downhill, but fire will burn uphill. It's unwise to move very far away from the crash site, though, because search-and-rescue crews have an exponentially harder task the farther away a victim travels. Rarog trains us in search-and-rescue policy so we know when help is likely to arrive and what forms it might take. "Even if you're pretty sure someone's on the way, prepare to spend the night," he says. "No pilot in the North is going to laugh at you if they find you setting up a lean-to. You've got to mentally prepare for survival and start working."

So I do. I set up a frame of dead trees roped across standing ones. I hack spruce boughs from the woods and haul them back to serve both as wind block and mattress. I dig a firepit and start some water boiling—we've been warned of the dangers of dehydration when everything that should be wet is frozen instead. None of the food I've brought is edible at this temperature except for the trail mix which contains nuts I can warm up enough to chew. The granola bars in my pack would break my teeth. The rubbery plastic dry bag I keep my clothes in disintegrates as I try to uncrumple it, snapping like brittle toffee. Rarog comes by to let me know I haven't quite oriented the lean-to properly in relation to the firepit and the wind, but by this point I'm too tired to adjust it. I have discovered, however, that no matter how cold it is, extended bouts of hard physical labour are just the thing. My parka even became too warm at one point.

I settle in for the night, burrowing into my sleeping bag and turning away from the fire to face the inside of my shelter, watching my breath fog around my nose, warming it momentarily. As I drift into a chilly drowsiness, I dread the inevitable refuelling demands of the fire. I hope the woodpile I've built will carry me through the night, because as the darkness descends around 3 P.M., it becomes very difficult to see the twigs in front of my face while walking. It would be a hassle to have to forge a path in the dark into the areas not yet picked over by other members of the group.

I'm not alone in my fireside slumber—around the world, families and communities are doing the same. Granted, they're mostly at lower latitudes, warmed by multiple sleeping companions of all ages and in close proximity to domesticated animals. Sleeping by a fire is a fine art, and the experienced fireside sleeper can awake effortlessly, unconsciously cued by a slight change in background noise. An overall reduction in volume suggests the fire is burning low, and loud popping suggests it's hit a patch of wetter or sappier wood. Somehow, people manage to get a full night's sleep while subliminally monitoring the fire sounds and getting up periodically to refuel and tend the blaze. Mothers have to be hypervigilant to ensure that their children aren't exposed to overheating; burn scars from stray flinders or a spreading fire are common in communities that sleep this way.

For me, air quality is the issue, and the nagging headache I assumed was dehydration builds through the night into a pounding throb caused by smoke inhalation. The night is exhausting, and I'd be surprised if I logged much more than an hour's fragmented rest. And this is the fortunate scenario—the one where I've landed around trees I'm able to burn and use for shelter. I've got food with me and a stove and a pot and an axe and string; none of those things would likely be around in an actual emergency—say, if my Ski-Doo broke down in the middle of a long ride.

At six in the morning, we're called away from our fireside lean-tos. Chad is missing. The news is met by confused and groggy faces. "This is a drill, obviously," says Rarog, as comprehension dawns among the mock survivors. We find Chad lying in the forest, where he's been gathering firewood. He's hypothermic. The exhausted medevac nurse takes the lead on this assignment, instructing all hands to help our patient to the fire, disrobe him and prepare zip-lock bags full of hot water to tuck in beside him. ("Umm, I think the bag by my foot is leaking," says Chad, breaking out of his faux unconsciousness long enough to curse his soggy socks.) Only ten kilometres away from Yellowknife, the outdoor classroom gets crystal-clear cellphone reception, but each "survivor" makes a practice call on the iridium satellite phone, surprising family members at home with our upbeat voices.

Then it's on to the next task. If I'm stranded in the middle of the tundra, my only hope is to get under the snow. Our second night is spent in a snow house, or *quinzhee*, constructed over seven hours of work with shovels (also an unlikely tool to have on hand in a real emergency). Quinzhees are back-breaking to prepare, but if I can't get under the snow, I won't survive a night above the treeline. The women are trying to keep hydrated, but we're reluctant to drink much because we know we're supposed to relieve ourselves into zip-lock bags tonight, so as not to disturb the snow blockade at our quinzhee's entrance.

It's a claustrophobic feeling, testing out the quinzhee. However, once I'm parked on the sleeping platform inside, cushioned by a layer of spruce boughs, I feel the insulating power of the snow. It's deadly silent in here, and I wonder if my sleeping neighbours could hear me scream if there was a cave-in. The only light comes from my survival candle and headlamp, plus a dim beam descending from a ventilation hole. With no campfires to stoke and no wind to blow through my mattress, I realize with relief it will be a much better night's sleep than I had in my lean-to.

Back outside, with the second evening drawing to a close, we light the signal pyres we built earlier. Dozens of spruce trees are suspended in a tripod frame, and when the fuel cup ignites, a gust of air from below turns the structure into a flame-thrower. A metre-wide column of fire shoots into the sky and sparks rain down from the heavens. I know Rarog wants to make sure that if I ever face death in the wilderness—years from now, perhaps—I will not go gently into that good night. The next morning, I head home with the conviction that in an actual emergency I would probably die. I take a couple of Tylenols for my cracking headache and sleep through the day in my warm, Western, human-atypical bed.

Even those nights in the woods were not a faithful model of how ancestral people would have experienced sleeping in the elements. For one thing, we had flashlights and bright fire. The strength of the moonlight and full exposure to plunging nighttime temperatures did not fully come into play.

My earliest immersion in a non-Western culture was as part of Canada World Youth, a program that pairs a group of Canadian teens with a group of teens from another country—in our case, an Egyptian counterpart. The combined team lived together and worked on various community-development projects, like planting grasses along Prince Edward Island beaches to stave off shore erosion. There was a buddy system, and my partner Ranya and I volunteered at a rarely visited art gallery attached to the famous *Anne of Green Gables* musical production. Beyond the obvious mismatch between Canadian teen culture and the priorities of Islam, there were countless small divergences. For one thing, Ranya was unaccustomed to household pets. For the Canadians, a common theme, unexpectedly, was the sanctity of sleep. Once asleep, a North American is likely to be, if not tiptoed around, at least left undisturbed unless there is some type of emergency. In contrast, if I retired at ten in Egypt, I might be woken at midnight by someone asking where I had put the spatula. I started to wonder why I had ever thought sleep was a state deserving of respect. Perhaps it is only when a society becomes chronically sleep deprived that hours of it are hoarded and jealously guarded from disruption.

This is borne out in the research. Solitary sleep on a softly cushioned surface between four walls and under a roof is hardly typical. Anthropologist Carol Worthman has spent many years in the field studying nighttime in traditional societies. In contrast with the Western sleep model—a regular bedtime followed by continuous sleep until morning—the Efe of Congo have some level of social activity persisting through all hours. The sleeping area of a family will see coming and going as some members retire and others hear the familiar strains of a thumb piano and get up to dance.

The Kalahari Desert's !Kung have similarly staggered bedtimes in their two-metre-circumference huts made of sticks and leaves. The huts aren't much of an insulator for heat, sound or predators—

they mostly just keep the rain off—and it's easy to feel embedded in the social interaction outside the hut. This set-up lends itself to a less defined difference between sleeping and waking. Adults and children alike stay up as long as something interesting is going on, and it's perfectly acceptable to check out of a group conversation by going to sleep. It's a convenient way of cutting short an interminable or circular argument that's become frustrating. Though sleepers won't be woken at random, no one makes a particular effort to be quiet around sleeping people. Groups of men use the pre-dawn quiet to debate, chat and settle disputes, like who's hogging the food supplies or who might be having an affair.

Daily work has a big effect on sleep, which must be fit in around survival tasks. In many societies, women have the most grinding labour and are glad to rest as soon as the evening meal is eaten, even if the men are staying up to socialize. Malnutrition worsens this lethargy after a calorically demanding day. There's a certain amount of truth to the fairy-tale image of a shepherd snoozing under a tree at noon. After early morning grazing allows his herd to take in the cool dew, a pastoralist might take advantage of the heat to keep the herd from wandering while he naps. Nighttime milking will lead to a late bedtime, so what sleep scientists call a *biphasic* (two-part) sleep schedule functions best for this type of herding work.

The amount of sleep we need is exceeded by the hours of darkness in a typical night, but during the period of darkness we cannot safely or effectively carry out many daytime activities. Gathering food, for example, would be unwise as nighttime colour perception is not good enough to distinguish between an edible berry and a poisonous one, and straying from the group for this purpose leaves a person vulnerable to predators. Instead, socializing tends to be the nighttime focus outside of sleep hours. The Efe groom each other to remove parasites that might disturb their sleep.

If there's a full moon, the !Kung might have a special dance late at night to celebrate a recent rainfall, and the whole community

A SPIRITED OCCASION

Japan's Festival for the Spirits of the Dead is a three-night window—around the time of the seventh moon in the lunar calendar—when the dead revisit the living world. In contrast to our Halloween, which is in some ways similar, the tone of the festival is not at all creepy. Welcome fires are lit in front of household entrances to light the way for ancestral guests. The householder jumps over the fire to invite the guests in, and then another fire on the last night sends them back out.

will sleep it off the next day. Commonalities in nocturnal celebrations are uncanny. The festivals (think of all the pagan events whose names end with "eve") are often derived from relief at nature cooperating with its expected patterns. When the harvest comes or the prey animals arrive as predicted by traditional calendars, it means a much greater probability of security and survival for the group. Many cultures incorporate their ancestors and deceased loved ones into nocturnal festivals, where dim visibility increases the chances of seeing ambiguous visions. Fire is a mainstay of such occasions, and leaping over a fire is surprisingly popular in a variety of traditions.

A dear friend of mine in middle school was the daughter of an anthropologist. She would come back from months on Groote Eylandt, off the northern shores of Australia, with stories about the tribe she had lived with—indeed, was a part of, there. I'd make her repeat their name—Anindilyakwa—until I could master saying it. She talked about having a totem animal that encompassed all kinds of dangerous snake species and how it meant you couldn't eat them. Photos of her with the last Song Man—custodian of spiritual knowledge and songs and stories of the spirit world, or *Dreamtime*—were proof of her adventures, as was her father's vast collection of didgeridoos, reputed to be the largest assemblage in North America of the Aboriginal wind instruments.

Her father, David Turner, started his ethnography of the people on Groote Eylandt in 1969. I took one of his classes when he was head of the anthropology department at the University of Toronto and learned that the recordings he'd made of rituals, dances and songs in the 1970s had played a major part in a later cultural resurgence. Upon his return to the island more than a decade later, he played back his tapes and the elders were astonished—they had lost the group memory of these cultural treasures as their oral history degenerated and the youth no longer learned the traditional language. In 1986, Turner underwent the second stage of initiation and was asked to represent his new people to the world.

He represented them too well for some of his colleagues' liking. "Anthropologists pay lip service to empathy with Aboriginal world views, but they never seem to actually do it," he observes. "If you step over the line, it becomes unacceptable to them. But that's what you're supposed to do! Believe it—step into it." He argues that anthropologists used to assimilate fully into their host cultures, but that the advent of universal theories of culture interfered with anthropologists' ability to relate to other ways of thinking. This makes him both a throwback and a post-postmodernist.

He's not too worried about—and is even a little bit grateful for—his field's dismissal of his work. He's enjoyed tenure for decades, so his position at the university is never in question. It means he can now proceed in peace with no one bothering to attack his publications, and he's content with the thought that sometimes it takes a long time for the world to discover what you've done. Sometimes it even happens after your death. Meanwhile, ever since he decided to teach his classes exactly what he feels to be true, his course evaluations have been out of this world.

He is a strong advocate for acknowledging Western civilization's shortfalls and touts the Australian Aboriginal cultures as having a more advanced world view for peacemaking. For example: they practise a philosophy of renunciation, whereby everything a person owns must be given to someone who needs it. Turner argues that over the long history of Aboriginal people in Australia, they have considered and consciously rejected Western notions—like individual possessions, technology and property—in favour of explicit mutual interdependence and environmental harmony. Even though the Aboriginals' lack of theft, social classes and relative poverty were clear evidence of this, some found it hard to accept the thought that a traditional society might be more sophisticated than our own in many ways.

Turner's recent work involves Inuit art and shamanism in Pangnirtung, Nunavut. He observes that traditional Inuit sleep in groups, partly as a matter of warmth in the cold climate. The unforgiving polar environment didn't allow for any wasted time or energy when the men went out to hunt or the women to fish. When a group went out to hunt seal or whale, they wouldn't come back or sleep until they got what they'd gone out for. Day and night were all the same while they patiently pursued their catch, and when they arrived home triumphant they might sleep for two days. Summer and winter alike—though in winter they had the advantage of the polar bears not competing with them for the same prey—the Inuit had to be keenly aware of the rhythms of the walrus, the pupping of the seals.

The Australian Aboriginal tribe Turner belongs to approached subsistence-living rhythms differently from the Inuit. In the baking sun, they'd die of dehydration if they worked all day, so when on the land, they'd have a *polyphasic* half-day cycle. After sleeping from eleven in the morning until three or four in the afternoon, like a siesta, they'd get up for the evening, but nap again after the sun went down. Then they'd get up again, in the middle of the night, for their second day, this one more physically active than the last. The women, doing their plant gathering in the hot sun, had similar sleep habits.

In this polygamous society, the wives of a given man—usually sisters—sleep together, and the men separately or in a group. Men typically visit their wives, rather than living in the same dwelling with them.

Turner described taking part in these nocturnal hunting and fishing activities around the coastal community, always attuned to the dangers. Other than snakes, the main predator of concern was the saltwater crocodile, found in large numbers in the billabongs and estuaries of the river systems near Darwin, in Australia's Northern Territory. Anyone foolish enough to sleep on the beach could be snapped up, and even if he or she were awake, a croc can outrun a human within twenty metres. Propelled by their tails when they're out of the water, the crocodiles can sprint for a very short time across the beach, but then run out of explosive power, being such large reptiles. "They're really big, you wouldn't believe it," says Turner. "And [the people of the tribe] always made me the designated lookout while they went into the water. It was dumb, because I didn't have an eye for it at all." Even in freshwater billabongs that fed streams leading to the ocean, you had to scour the waterscape for the crocodiles, just their eyes sticking out of the water. There were sharks too, but most Aborigines didn't swim—a counterintuitive norm for seafaring cultures.

In some ways, though living in the tropics, the Aborigines of northern Australia lived as seasonal a lifestyle as Arctic people. During the rainy season, the sheer force of the downpour prevented them from venturing outside. Even if they had, the water was too murky to fish in. For a crash course in the political theory behind this type of traditional knowledge, I consulted a neighbourhood author.

Stephanie Irlbacher-Fox knows how to tan a moosehide and, in her line of work, this gets her far more respect than her Cambridge PhD. Barefoot and glamorous in her chic, open-concept kitchen-dining-living room—renovating houses is a family hobby—Fox flips easily between explaining political theory and tending to an under-the-weather two-year-old. ("Do you want to draw?" "*No!*" "Do you want to draw with [your big brother's] markers?" Approving silence.) Fox has spent her career advising northern Canadian Aboriginal groups on self-government issues and helping to negotiate land claims. The work has left her adamant about a cultural revival that needs to take place if colonial powers are to be staved off.

Insight arrived when she realized Canada's policies were simultaneously devastating indigenous people, blaming them for their own suffering and billing the government as a source of salvation. Colonial attitudes are insidious, like the assumption that Canada would naturally be the dominant party in negotiations with Aboriginal groups. In her book *Finding Dahshaa*—which was held in peer review for three years because of its fringe views—she claims that the Canadian government has predetermined outcomes in place when it enters into self-government negotiations with indigenous peoples and that the whole process amounts to theatre. Instead of self-government on the country's terms, Irlbacher-Fox advocates self-determination and a cultural resurgence that would see traditional birth, child care, community decision-making and justice practices reinstated.

In history, in order for Canada to exist, indigenous people had to be gotten out of the way. "The settlers who came to this land were the dregs of society," she says. "I mean, read Christopher Columbus's diaries—he was a raping, pillaging, drunken sailor." What she takes from this is a deep humility when the elders in the villages invite her to do research with them and a sense of responsibility not to be another white person who screws them over.

She warns me that associating people's indigenousness with a quality of "pastness" is a colonial attitude. She routinely rids herself of these thoughts through a process of personal decolonization. There's been a history of Aboriginal people being told that their cultures are backward, that they should stop clinging to the past and "progress" toward integration in the larger society. I start to worry that for me to lump in traditional societies with our own civilization's history certainly could suggest that I agree with this notion of progress—the idea that societies naturally aspire to higher technology, individualism and perpetual growth.

To my surprise, David Turner disagrees with Stephanie Irlbacher-Fox. Rather than taking exception to indigenousness having a quality of pastness, he asserts this is the very definition of it: "Indigenous means in continuity with the past: an unbroken line of something." He says he gets fed up with mainstream anthropology's pseudo-Marxist take at the moment and feels it doesn't explain much more than colonialism. As an activist he's a bigger fan of getting out there and helping indigenous people avoid oppression than of talking about how oppressed they are. He also assures me I can use hunter-gatherer tribes in a given place as a useful analogue for ancestral humans in the same area of the world, as the environment's patterns are more or less the same now as they were under ancestral conditions. Of course, you cannot predict from contemporary traditional societies how our ancestors married or what their beliefs might have been, and so on.

It's therefore important that I clarify my reasons for combining history and prehistory with pastoral and hunter-gatherer models in the modern world as part of my search for our original cultural responses to circadian rhythms. First, people living in equatorial regions, intimately familiar with the local ecosystem's complexities, share that familiarity with ancestral humans. Looking at the experiences of people living today with minimal technology offers an analogue for pre-industrial life, and this is something I must do if I'm to understand daily rhythms in times past. Of course, sophisticated kinship groups, rich oral histories and innumerable other cultural wealth separates the present from the far past. What some societies have either chosen not to adopt or have been prevented by circumstance from instituting they have amply replaced with other values, be they spiritual systems, intricate mythologies or traditional medicines. The skill set of a modern-day hunter is infinitely better informed in some ways than that of those who've shared his calling in the past. But the overall environmental constraints these groups deal with are similar. The parameters of life on the land are what our bodies—including our circadian rhythms—evolved to cope with.

Secondly, for convenience, I simply demonstrate the wide variety of cultural practices relating to sleep and other rhythms throughout history as well as around the world. The !Kung practice of working out disputes in the wee hours is as unfamiliar and foreign to most of this book's readers as the medieval English practice of "second sleep." The point I'd like to communicate is that there are many ways people around the world and through time have found to accommodate and evade their rhythmic natures. As with anything cultural, the genius of humankind has been to experiment and pass on what works in the span of single lifetimes; scheduling practices have diverged radically from each other, tied together only by their common biological basis. I hope this suffices to quell most objections to my comparing societies past and present: I'm aware of the awkward relationship between today's traditional societies and our ancestral counterparts, and I'm combining them anyway, but with caution.

In the cramped alcove that serves as Fox's home office, parenting books stand beside back issues of *Arctic* journal. On the wall, a photo of Fox in front of crossed oars serves as a memento of her days as stroke of Magdalene College Cambridge Women's 3rd VIII rowing team. She speaks of her PhD period at Cambridge as a formative experience, with aspects strangely reminiscent of northern Canada's indigenous culture. "We weren't being marked, so social norms were how you figured out how well you were doing," says Fox. "And rather than sticking to a timetable, it was sequencing that was important. That's something you find in the indigenous communities too." At Cambridge, each item of business was addressed in turn, and if people got hungry, the class simply ambled down to the local pub and continued there. Likewise, in elders' forums, an agenda is often set and each subject discussed for as long as it takes, not according to a pre-arranged time window.

It's sequencing that allows indigenous cultures to predict with stunning accuracy the natural events around them. The circannual rhythms of each plant and animal can be set on a timeline so that the salmon run might coincide every year with the budding of a given constellation of plants. But climate change is confounding large bodies of traditional knowledge as day length decouples from temperature and as plants and animals drift away from their migratory routes and reproductive schedules. Animal ranges are creeping up in latitude and plant growth happens earlier in the year. The difference in temperature between the day and the night is muted now.

Of course, life in traditional northern communities is still dictated by season. As a journalist I was often told I couldn't reach elders in September because they'd likely be on the land, hunting for caribou, or at their fishing camps. Cranberry-picking is a favourite pastime for women and children at this time of year. In living memory is a time when summer and winter were like one long day and night.

Elders in northern Canada recall that summers were a time of almost manic hunting and working activity, with very little sleep. The starlit winters were for staying indoors, eating from the meat cache and enjoying one's family. Many communities still create communal meat-storage areas by digging deep into the permafrost, where the temperature is constant—cold enough to keep meat frozen, but not extremely cold like the air outside.

We think of the Inuit as the people who have most impressively survived extreme seasonality with a minimum of resources. But long before Inuit arrived in the eastern Arctic, a very different culture thrived there. They were known as the Dorset people, and they disappeared in the fourteenth century—or so it's thought ...

For the better part of the past five thousand years, the eastern Arctic was populated by the shy, peace-loving Dorset. They lacked the Inuit's specialized gadgets and whaling tradition, concentrating on walrus and seal instead. Rather than building igloos wherever they settled, they travelled with skin tents, which they banked with snow or sod. The archaeological record shows no further traces of the Dorset or their unique shamanic world view after the Inuit arrived from the West. But rumours abound of Dorset survivors who somehow escaped the mysterious fate of their people.

The workings of oral history are a bit like the newspaper business: If it bleeds, it leads. War and conflict are sure to get a mention around the evening fire, but harmony and intermarriage between peoples can get left out of the storytelling. Anthropologist Susan Rowley was a young researcher when she travelled to Iglulik in search of stories from the elders. She asked about the original Arctic people—the Dorset—and what happened to them when the Inuit moved into the area. "I was too young to know when I was asking a silly question," she remembers, and her ignorance of contemporary conventional wisdom paid off. "I sat in this elder's house hearing about the killings, and at one point, I said, 'But weren't there intermarriages with the Dorset?' She replied 'Of course there were, but who's going to talk about *them*?'" The encounter stuck with Rowley throughout her career.

Shortly after 3000 BCE, a group of humans crossed over from Siberia and took up residence all across the North American Arctic and Greenland. Their way of life seems similar to that of some Siberian people at the time, down to the design of their homes, which bear similarities to those of modern Sami. With a stone-paved central passageway their conical tents had a box hearth at the centre and were divided into halves roughly two metres in radius. "Uncovering old Dorset house sites gives you the best sense of who these people were," says Rowley. "I have my students draw how they imagine people lived, based on where there were needles, where we found matting for beds." Tiny bird-bone needles with drilled eyes remain as a testament to sophisticated Dorset tailoring. Well-preserved carvings depict high-collared, layered parkas and high boots with skin pants. Dogs were not employed in the same ways that Inuit use them.

The Dorset had the run of the Arctic, with all its fresh resources—centuries' worth of driftwood and animals unused to humans—for the next four thousand years. Then came the Vikings. "The Norse established colonies in the tenth century, and there are lots of objects showing up in Dorset sites to suggest that contact was extensive and complex," says Pat Sutherland, curator of Arctic archaeology at the Canadian Museum of Civilization. Pieces of white pine—itself a rare driftwood find in the Arctic—were found with iron-stained holes made by square nails. Though the spinning of wool was not a technique used in the Arctic, lengths of spun yarn were found at Dorset sites at Nunguvik on Baffin Island, made out of Arctic hare and goat hair. Both were radiocarbon dated to the late thirteenth or early fourteenth centuries.

Fascinating but less scientifically verifiable evidence came from antler wands or batons that showed European-like faces: straight noses, prominent eyebrows, even beards and Viking-like caps. "The problem is, Dorset portraits often featured transformational figures, suggesting a shamanistic world," warns Sutherland. "But our evidence is the Norse were indeed after the Dorset walrus-hunting expertise." This time period coincides with the highest Norse demand for ivory and Arctic animal fur, and a twelfth-century Norse text, *Historia Norvegiae*, describes a people living beyond Greenland, whom it called Skraelings. "They do not know the use of iron, but employ walrus tusks as missiles and sharpened stones in place of knives," reads the text. It would be several decades before the Norse encountered the Inuit, so it's likely these Skraelings were Dorset. The text goes on to describe an anomaly: "When they are struck with a weapon their wounds turn white and they do not bleed." As the Norse wore cloth, rather than the more blade-resistant animal skins of the Dorset, they may have been puzzled by these bloodless wounds they inflicted.

As we track the current imposition of Western—and, in particular, American—customs and culture across the globe, it is instructive to remember this is but the latest repetition of history and prehistory. For any given environment there are myriad ways to adapt a human community to the habitat. Human ingenuity has devised multiple lifestyles that suit the extremely seasonal climate of the Arctic, and each successive wave of immigration to the region has brought with it competing methods of seasonal coping. The Inuit who in this past century have settled in communities, dropping their seasonal nomadic rhythms in favour of centrally heated housing and imported groceries, were themselves at one time the cultural dominators of a smaller, more well-established people.

If the Dorset really didn't know the use of iron when they first encountered the Norse, they discovered its uses very rapidly, along with copper from deposits in the Coppermine region. Meteorites in northwest Greenland yielded iron that could be traded with the Norse or used as carving tools in the creation of the signature Dorset miniature sculptures. Rumours of these riches in the hands of the Dorset may have led to their eventual ruin. "The Dorset may have communicated that there was metal to the east," postulates Sutherland. The promise of iron and copper could have been enough to draw whale hunters from Alaska—who managed the iron trade across the Bering Strait—across the barren channels of the central Arctic.

These ancestral Inuit are called Thule (*Too-lee*), and their earliest eastern Arctic sites are, indeed, found around a meteorite strike. The Thule brought along dogsleds, umiaks and a tradition of warfare. When they encountered the Dorset people, they named them Tuniit. The Inuit oral history recounts how the Inuit killed the Tuniit and drove them away from their camps, taking occupation of their land. "The last identified Dorset sites show that they were eating a restricted diet, consisting of lots of Arctic hare, but not caribou," says Rowley. "This suggests they were pushed out of good hunting spots into marginal areas." She adds that these may have been only the small bands of Tuniit who fled the Thule invasion rather than surrender and integrate.

At this point, when the medieval warm period delayed winter freezing and led to unpredictable climates and open water, the Dorset way of life may have already been stressed to the point of vulnerability. The archaeological sites predating their disappearance in the record turn up a proliferation of amulets—charms to guard against a demise they may have sensed was in the offing.

The tale of the beleaguered Tuniit was passed through Inuit generations long after the Dorset disappearance. In 1922, Inuit historian Ivaluardjuk told explorer Knud Rasmussen of the last Tuniit in Foxe Basin, who had been driven out of their villages by overwhelming numbers of armed Inuit. An appealing side note to the story brightens the sorry ending: Tradition holds that one solitary band of Tuniit survived the onslaught and took up residence well apart from the Inuit to continue their way of life. They were called the Sadlermiut, and they lived on three islands in northern Hudson Bay: Walrus, Coats and Southampton.

A mere handful of families, they lived apart from the surrounding Inuit, in stone and sod houses, using Tuniit-style stone tools and speaking a strange dialect. In place of the ubiquitous kayak, the Sadlermiut rode inflated sealskins and walrus skins and wore oddly cut clothes.

Alas, a Scottish whaling crew set up shop on Southampton Island in 1899, and some of the Sadlermiut—by then numbering fewer than a hundred—made the mistake of visiting the whalers' shore station at the southern tip of the island. Two years later, a whaler came ashore with a nasty form of dysentery that spread to the Sadlermiut camps and killed every last one in a matter of months.

Many archaeologists dispute the notion that these Sadlermiut were Dorset survivors. "I wouldn't take it too far. They could have just been Thule people discovering Dorset items," says Sutherland. "The Inuit describe the Tuniit as the ones who 'made the land habitable for us by building the caribou drives and fish weirs.'"

Susan Rowley points out that many of the differences noticed, particularly in language, stem from comparing the Sadlermiut to the geographically closest groups of Inuit. "They are usually compared with the people on the west coast of Hudson Bay, but their contacts were actually with the Inuit on south Baffin Island. And those are the people we find talking about the Sadlermiut," she says.

Sadlermiut differences might have come from their environment, which was bereft of the slate and soapstone used in Thule tools. But some observers argued that the difference in material culture was too stark: The Sadlermiut couldn't be just an aberrant band of luddite Thule.

Meanwhile, geneticist Geoffrey Hayes tackled the question from a different angle. "There are a number of interesting examples in the archaeological record where we see a sharp transition," he says. "The natural assumption is that this represents a new people coming in and overtaking, but the only way to know for sure is to genetically test."

Then a PhD student at the University of Utah, Hayes finagled permission from the Inuit Heritage Trust to remove fingernail-sized pieces from the ribs of ancient skeletons. There were four sample groups—the Thule, the Dorset, the Sadlermiut and modern-day Inuit. It's a tall order to find a decent pool of Dorset remains, probably because their burial practices involved lowering bodies through a hole in the ice or returning them to the sea; Hayes's dissertation work suffered from having only a tiny sample of Dorset—three individuals.

Nevertheless, his findings hinted at something startling. His lab looked at a type of DNA passed down only by a person's mother (mitochondrial DNA). "North American Aboriginal people descend from four of these lineages—A, B, C and D—and most populations share a mix of all four," says Hayes. "But Inuit are almost all from type A, which suggests their population has always been relatively small." A mere 2 percent of Inuit are type D. Hayes looked at his twenty Thule samples, dated to a thousand years ago from the western shores of Hudson Bay. Since *Thule* is just another name for Inuit who lived before European contact, he wasn't surprised to see the results all come up type A. The two-thousand-year-old Dorset ribs told a different story. They were all type D, completely unrelated to modern-day Inuit. "So it does look like the Thule were a new population coming in—the Dorset didn't just suddenly figure out how to whale," says Hayes.

As for the thirty-five Sadlermiut—the youngest skeletons, at between 200 and 400 years old—their DNA revealed a fifty-fifty split between type A and type D. "It's possible the Sadlermiut were neither remnant Dorset nor aberrant Thule," says Rowley. "They may have been a mixed group with a relatively small number of Thule." While the group adopted the Thule ways of cairn burials and whale hunting, they might have had enough Dorset influence to make them visibly unusual.

Whoever these people were, Susan Rowley knows an alternate ending to the Sadlermiut story of which even Dr. Hayes was unaware. Her father, Graham Rowley, one of the last great Arctic explorers, travelled to the area in the 1930s as an archaeologist on a British expedition. On Southampton Island, he excavated Sadlermiut sites. He also learned that one family—a woman and her four children—had escaped the fate of the others and lived through the turn of the century. They were taken in by the Inuit who worked at the whaling station.

Graham Rowley's memoirs describe one day in 1939, when he visited a group of Inuit on Jens Munk Island: five families living in two igloos. A man named Kinga was among them, and Rowley learned that Kinga was one of those adopted children, the last of the Sadlermiut. He was described as a little above average height, but in other ways just one of his adoptive Inuit family.

§

The Kennedy era saw radical changes to American education, starting with math and physics. Paranoid over Russian superiority in science after Sputnik's launch, the country threw itself into reforming teaching methods to give its kids an edge on the international stage. The educational crisis eventually engendered more holistic curriculum reform that expanded to cover the social sciences. Given free rein to revamp social studies for grades five and six, pedagogy turned experimental with "Man, A Course of Study" (known as MACOS).

Development of the course started in 1963 and, after test runs in three hundred classrooms, it was let loose on four hundred thousand American ten-year-olds in seventeen hundred schools across forty-seven states. Central to the year-long MACOS curriculum was a film series shot in Pelly Bay, in what is now Nunavut, among the Netsilingmiut. Pelly Bay had just built its first houses, but most of the community still lived in igloos, and land-based knowledge still thrived. The footage captured scenes of seal hunting with sled dogs, traditional methods and tools, and fur clothing. Drum dances, games and spear fishing appeared exactly as they were practised. In particular, the series loosely followed a year in the life of a family there, recreating pre-contact life that was still in living memory.

Eschewing authoritative narration that would explain what the viewer was seeing, the movies held only sounds from kayak paddles in the water, wind over the tundra and Inuktitut voices in conversation. An Inuk mother used an ulu to slice bits of raw meat and feed them, warm, into her child's eager mouth. Students had as much of the ethnographer's experience as is possible in a classroom, figuring out for themselves the significance of what they were seeing and being immersed in a culture dramatically foreign to them.

Explorer and anthropologist Knud Rasmussen had stayed in Pelly Bay in 1922 and recorded extensive journals about the community there, the people's way of life and beliefs. MACOS sought to import ethnographic subjects such as Rasmussen's into the classroom. It was the surest way to combat racism and ethnocentrism. At the forefront of research, the children became the knowledge generators—a radical shift from the predigested information in social science textbooks that preceded it.

"I really was fishing. I needed food for my dogs," says one of the film's participants who enacted a spear-fishing scene. "Even though it was acting, it was the real thing." The anthropologists, including one the community nicknamed The Man Who Likes Old Things, told the Pelly Bay community to expect what seemed to be happening everywhere—a gradual disappearance of their way of life. They became complicit in recording their own knowledge for the generation raised with snowmobiles instead of dogsleds. "I remember when we started to live in houses," says Barthelemy Nirlungayak in the NFB documentary *Through These Eyes*, about the MACOS program. "I remember everything started to speed up. We had to start rushing around." Now the people who were included in the documentaries use the films to show their children how things were.

The program was exciting and effective—perhaps too effective. Children started demonstrating an intellectual flexibility that scared some of the adults around them, whom they had outstripped in open-mindedness. Engaged in classroom discussions like never before, the students trotted home and regaled their parents with stories of the small Inuit boy they'd seen eating an eyeball and of the caribou bladder that was blown into a balloon before their very eyes. To kids unused to seeing meat outside the grocery store in unpackaged form, some of the graphic images were disturbing, and there was a lot of nervous giggling around the more gory hunting scenes. Earlier MACOS units included a section on general biology, as well as one on baboon behaviour, and the Netsilik series was meant to present humanity as a *part* of nature.

Here was a culture that believed in spirits that lived under the sea and that engaged in shamanistic rituals. At ten years old, the children watching the films in schools were just young enough to be able to rapidly relate to the Inuit family, but just old enough to analyze and question their own possibly arbitrary and bizarre beliefs. If they could see their own values from the other point of view, they also began to see other cultures as equivalent to their own. Teachers asked questions like "How did you come to have your beliefs?" and let the classroom discussion erupt into heated debate. It was this cultural relativism that really stirred up the public's distrust.

Phoenix congressman John Conlan alleged the curriculum advocated wife-sharing, infanticide, senicide and communal living (that last one apparently as ideologically scary as the others). The ensuing controversy led to congressional hearings that shut down the MACOS program. In 1981, the textbooks were pulled. Since MACOS implementation, the Apollo moon landing had taken urgency away from the perceived education gap between USSR and United States, and the wave of curriculum reform had subsided.

In contrast, the subjects of the Netsilik Eskimo Series take a more trusting view of their children's education. "It hurts my heart when people say that youth are stupid and don't know what they are doing. I think young people are smart. They've been to school," says Ovide Allakannuak in *Through These Eyes*. "Many know both Inuktitut and English. If they don't know what they're doing now, they will learn. We will teach them."

Distrust of all things different, especially when they threaten our core cultural beliefs, is instinctive and not easily overcome. It has led to a wave of cultural imperialism, whereby traditional cultures are brought into Western lifestyles with a missionary zeal—even when religion itself is not involved. And it has homogenized the world's daily schedules to mind-numbing, year-round, grinding shift work, oblivious to local conditions and latitude, oblivious to the quotidian rituals that define culture and constitute valuable knowledge transmitted down the generations. Seasonality is all but gone in urban centres, and the remaining pockets of environmentally responsive living will surely follow.

FIVE

between first and second sleep

Forget for a second the fact that so many people now routinely complain of sleep deprivation, and forget the mania of our go-go-go society. Instead, look for a moment at our intuitive understanding of what's best—the eight-hour night of solid sleep. Psychiatrist Thomas Wehr conducted sleep experiments that confirmed that when the lights are switched off for eight hours a night, people sleep more or less straight through—so far, consistent with conventional wisdom. But eight hours of darkness is found in a natural setting only during summer in the temperate zones. The rest of the time and in the rest of the places in the absence of artificial light, night easily can last twelve or fourteen hours. So what would our bodies naturally do under these circumstances? Wehr shut off the lights for fourteen hours a night and watched. Continuing to fall asleep soon after lights out and to wake up when they were switched back on, the subjects settled into an expanded sleep that encompassed the new night, but with a fascinating exception:

There were a couple of hours in the middle of the night when they were awake, peacefully thinking in bed.

A month with no artificial light leads to a different body chemistry—something I find worrying because of what natural processes we may be missing out on—with high melatonin and growth hormone through the night from a much earlier hour. Sleep itself becomes reliably two-phase. Asleep by eight o'clock, subjects woke up around midnight and rested in bed, reflecting quietly and daydreaming until about two in the morning. They rose again at six to greet the dawn. A curious surge of prolactin (the same hormone that causes relaxation after sex) accompanied the waking interlude, which accounts for the self-reflective, meditative state subjects described. In the days after these long two-phase sleeps, the subjects remarked in wonder that they'd never in their lives felt so awake. They realized that they had not only caught up on their sleep, but also were feeling true wakefulness for the first time.

Two four-hour sleep blocks with a kind of inverse siesta in the wee hours was the norm in Western history too. In early modern England, for example, only the rich could afford candles and rush lights, so most people went to bed with the sun. Night air was seen as unhealthy, so families shuttered their windows at dusk and retired soon after for what they called *first sleep*. After waking for prayer and quiescent activity in the dead of night, they embarked on their *morning sleep*, before waking for the day.

A friend has been transcribing an ancestor's memoirs from the nineteenth century. He came across the following passage: "I usually awaken at about 1:00 A.M. and think over the days gone by. When Mother was here we would both often awaken at this time in the morning. Then we would talk about the children who were scattered far away over the world. We would each offer a fervent prayer: 'God bless the dear children.' She would say, 'Good-night, Dear Husband, God give us sleep and rest.' Then we would turn over and go to sleep again." Right up until the

Industrial Revolution, first sleep and second sleep were standard practice, instead of a single, uninterrupted stay in bed.

Sleep has represented virtue as well as vice in various contexts throughout history. Prudently recharging one's batteries to awake refreshed and productive shares a fine line next to slothful self-indulgence and checking out of a full life. Sinful and saintly sleep can coexist, separated by the narrowest of differences. The Bible encompasses both interpretations: Compare "How long will you lie there, you sluggard? When will you get up from your sleep?" (Proverbs 10:5) with "In vain you rise early and stay up late, toiling for food to eat—for he grants sleep to those he loves." (Psalms 127:2). The notion continues in the present day that hard work induces a good sleep, while rich, idle men toss and turn. If that hard work were labour out of doors, modern science would support the popular wisdom, as a worker would have clearly defined day and night cues. Dozing away the day, however, has sometimes been a status symbol, a conspicuous disdain for the commoners' need to work. Poor sleep is often associated with a guilty conscience, and sound sleep—resting easy—with certainty in one's right actions.

When the Hebrew God is mentioned as sleeping, it is as a form of rejecting people—they beg him to wake up and return to them and to return them to his good graces. In contrast, the Quran is emphatic that Allah never sleeps: "No slumber can seize Him nor sleep. His are all things in the heavens and on earth ... He feeleth no fatigue in guarding and preserving them for He is the Most High, the Supreme in glory" (Surah 2:255).

Before humans measured time in ever-diminishing standard units, we always organized our days according to the time cues in nature. Jewish custom describes prayer when the cock crows, then again at noon and finally when on a clear night three stars can be discerned in the sky. If it's cloudy, there's an ingenious contingency method involving the human eye's transition to night vision. During the evening, our sight depends on the black-and-white-sensing photoreceptors of the retina, rather than on the cones that can pick up colours from more intense light. The final prayer can be made when a blue thread and a black thread look the same. Buddhist monks also have a kind of substitute for an alarm clock—when the veins in a hand held up to the sun are visible, it's time to get up. The cultural imperialism of the West has washed out a lot of the diversity in daily rituals of societies around the world.

Even a standard eight hours can have wildly different connotations depending on which eight hours one chooses to sleep through. "Early to bed and early to rise makes a man healthy, wealthy and wise," goes the saying. Whereas the morning lark apparently has intrinsic piety by behaving as the early bird catching the worm, night owls are notoriously dismissed as party animals, and sleeping late as lethargic and undisciplined.

TURNING BACK THE CLOCK

Springing forward and falling back are biannual equinox rituals in seventy countries. Societies that observe daylight savings time (DST) are attempting to extend their afternoon sunlight in wintertime. Confined to Western Europe and North America at the end of the twentieth century, the practice has seen an up-tick in popularity over the last few years with the former soviet countries, and even some more tropical nations have adopted the convention in the service of global synchrony.

Dissenters include Japan, where the American occupation once imposed the ritual. The Japanese soon rejected it, following farmers' complaints, and Japan's current department of education warns that schoolchildren might be tempted outside, away from their evening homework, should they start DST now. Arizona had a one-year experiment with it that resulted in an economic hit: The scorching state faced much higher air-conditioning expenses and quickly abandoned daylight savings.

This may be a holdover from agricultural days when dawn brought time-specific farm chores—milking according to the cows' circadian rhythms, for example—and when staying up late would only have been for social, and perhaps drinking, purposes. Side note: Cows' circadian rhythms have influenced government policy on at least one occasion. The Canadian province of Saskatchewan refuses to shift clocks for daylight savings time. The official reason: It disturbs the cows (in other words, it interrupts milk production in the days following the time shifts).

$$\text{\^{S}}$$

The times of day set aside for meals have also changed dramatically through the years, though the underlying digestive biology remains constant. Just as people from different cultures vary widely today in the number of meals they eat every day and the emphasis they place on each, those of us in the West have shifted our mealtimes in response to cultural imperatives. Caloric intake is the biological imperative, but there are many ways to fulfill that demand, and we've seemingly tried them all. In the Middle Ages, a light breakfast at the crack of dawn prepared peasants for a hard day's work, and lunch was the main meal. Supper, eaten just before dark, was simply a round of leftovers from lunch. In Shakespearean times, when farmers harvesting crops faced a long slog from lunch until summer sunset, there was a meal of bread and ale, called *nuntion*, in mid-afternoon. A turn-of-the-millennium diet craze, the Warrior Diet, claimed to be based on the ancestral meal timing of nomadic hunter-gatherers. Its creator, enterprising nutritionist Ori Hofmekler, proposed working and undereating during the day and then filling up at night as a way to become lean and strong.

❀

To see the importance of traditional knowledge in managing the Arctic's seasonal challenges, one need only look at what happens when Southerners live there, isolated. Without a cultural heritage of highly seasonal rhythms or a real sense of time cues, and without a regular sunrise and sunset, new Arctic residents are easily off-railed into free-running rhythms. John Blyth celebrated his twenty-sixth birthday in Norway's northern archipelago Svalbard, after living in total darkness through December and January, along with the other residents of Longyearbyen, its capital. At a latitude of 78 degrees, Longyearbyen is the northernmost permanent town on Earth (disregarding polar research stations and military outposts), and it's dark for longer than its latitude would suggest: Deep in a north-to-south valley with a sun-blocking glacier to the south, the town's winter night lasts from Thanksgiving until March 10.

Blyth and his girlfriend, Genevieve, pitched camp on the edge of town in a ten-by-ten-foot Arctic oven tent and took advantage of the unwritten local rule that coal from the nearby mines is freely available for personal heating use. They set up a coal-burning wood stove and enjoyed the wintry town, free from other tourists. Blyth integrated into the student community, playing a weekly game of kayak polo and frequenting the world's northernmost kebab shop. He quickly realized that his headlamp—a row of LED lights on an elasticated band—was sorely deficient for use ten or twelve hours a day. To see across the valley, the locals had Lupine-brand lamps with monster custom batteries, equivalent to wearing searchlights on their heads. Much like high-beam etiquette for night driving, it was considered polite to tilt your lamp downward when approaching another human.

Though not as extreme in climate as the Canadian Arctic, Svalbard has a challenging terrain and avalanches and polar bears to contend with. Locals walk around with 50-calibre handguns, and the bank has a sign imploring customers not to bring rifles onto the premises. The grocery store compromises with a cabinet out front to store your firearms as you shop. According to the Spitsbergen Treaty of 1920, the forty signing countries have equal rights to commercially exploit the islands, formerly an international territory much like Antarctica. Russia built coal-mining towns there, and there's a big Thai population, drawn by the jobs without work-permit requirements. In all other ways, Norway has sovereignty and develops its presence through a polar institute and a university. Blyth calls Svalbard a Norwegian fantasy island, where taxes are rock-bottom low and beer is half the price it is on the mainland.

Caribou near the poles switch off their circadian rhythms during the periods of perpetual day—instead, they structure their activities based on available food, and their rest periods are randomly distributed across the clock. Blyth describes a similar phenomenon during winter on Svalbard. His friends lost all track of time, especially during the Christmas school break, when a late night up at the bar could lead to a 7 P.M. sleep-in. Someone might go to bed at three in the morning while others were heading out to go skiing. Blyth would run into people on a different timeline and would have to ask what meal they'd just eaten, to coordinate plans. "When I didn't want to sleep, I was just so tired, and when I wanted to, I couldn't get to sleep," he recalls. But without a daily routine, he estimates he might have slept three-quarters of the day. "It was just so easy to sleep if you listened to your body," he says.

Meanwhile, the polar bears around him were undergoing their own seasonal changes. Only the pregnant females spend their winters in a den. Having mated in the summer, they hold on to the *blastula*, the little ball of cells that will become an embryo and that swims around in the uterus with no connection to the nutrient-giving womb wall. Only about four months later will the females allow the blastula to implant and continue its development into a cub, which will be born in the den after another four months. This is to ensure the weather will be warm enough when the cubs are raring to go out into the open air of the outside world. The male polar bear's scrotum descends in late winter, producing sperm starting in February, ready for when the females will appear. In late March, the mother and cubs emerge to restart their digestive systems and hunt vulnerable baby ringed seals on the permanent ice and harp seals birthing out on the pack ice. It's a particularly dangerous time for Svalbard's residents, potential victims of desperately hungry predators and fiercely protective mother bears.

When polar sunrise finally arrived, Blyth posted on Facebook: "Feb. 1: Saw the sun yesterday for the first time in two months. Darkness is only strange when you have light. If it's just dark all the time you just get used to it. Hell, we learned to tele-ski in the dark ... on a glacier. But seriously my eyes hurt, I feel like a vampire." The standard unit of illumination is the *lux* (luminous flux), where one lux is roughly equal to the light level of a full moon at a tropical latitude. Given that typical indoor surfaces are illuminated at fifty to five hundred lux, whereas a naturally lit landscape tends to reflect between five thousand and a hundred thousand lux, he can be forgiven for squinting. It was a day he'd literally been dreaming about, and the most startling change was being able to see for more than a couple of hundred metres in sharp resolution. When he describes it as the difference between black-and-white and colour, I realize there's a biological truth to this, in that the colour-sensing cones in his eyes would be engaged only with the help of the sunlight. Looking around, he realized how white everyone had become over the long, dark winter.

tick-tock

Wherever you are reading this, you are probably within easy sight of a clock. Maybe you're in a café with a clock on the wall. Maybe you're reading this on a computer screen with a digital time display in the corner. Maybe you wear a wristwatch or carry a phone on which you can always check the time. But if you keep a busy schedule, chances are that knowing the time is important to you and having a clock nearby helps you feel confident that you are keeping track of time. You may think this is unique to us as humans—after all, what appointments do plants and animals need to keep? But, in fact, all life forms carry their own clocks. All living things have their own ways of keeping themselves on schedule.

We think of clocks as man-made contraptions with an hour hand, a minute hand (big and little hands, we are first told as children) and perhaps one that counts off the seconds. If we're younger, we may think of clocks as digital readouts featuring two sets of two numbers, separated by a colon. But these displays, whatever form they take, are not really clocks at all. The clock part of them is usually hidden from view. In the case of the digital clock radio beside your bed, there's a glass crystal inside that changes its shape when an electric charge is sent through it. The change in shape produces a tiny sound at a regular frequency. The oscillations are registered by counters connected to chips that translate the signals to a readout. A clock is anything that has a regular cycle of motion, and in this case the clock is the glass crystal, producing regularly oscillating sound waves.

It's easier to see the constant motion in other clocks—think of the grandfather clock noisily swinging its pendulum in the corner of an otherwise silent room. Even as the pendulum's swing slows by friction to a narrower range, its period remains constant. But a clock can be a collection of candles of the same length, taking roughly the same time to burn. It can be an hourglass re-enacting the dynamics of falling sand again and again to mark similar time intervals. It can be a sundial displaying the very results of the planet's rotation that circadian rhythms all come down to.

The earliest known clock in Britain is the famous circle of enormous stones known as Stonehenge, arranged to catch the sun's movements and cast shadows accordingly. Nearby, in Salisbury Cathedral, the nation's oldest mechanical clock—still in working order—has been housed since its construction in 1386. A falling weight drives the wrought-iron mechanism and causes a bell to be rung every hour. This was the more efficient way to announce prayer times, the central structure of daily life in the village. Little did the clockmaker—whose name is lost to history—know that this would mark the beginning of the end of his era's cyclic view of time. From then on, the West would view time as linear, and this concept became one of the foundations of the Renaissance.

The medieval notion and measurement of time gave way to a modern view of time in the late seventeenth century, when Isaac

Newton published his groundbreaking *Principia Mathematica.* "Absolute, true, mathematical time, of itself, and from its own nature, flows equably without relation to anything external," he wrote. And with that, time was divorced from human history. The motions of all the heavenly bodies from Newton's time to our own were made accurately deductible from the elegant and immutable laws of universal gravitation and motion. The cosmos became one big clock-like mechanism.

After an interregnum of piety and oppression under Oliver Cromwell, King Charles II's flagrant debauchery and tolerance created the perfect cultural setting for scientific advancement. The Royal Society's meetings and discoveries stimulated considerable popular excitement. In Charles II's day, microscopes and telescopes were the latest must-have gadgets, akin to the iPhones of today, but the Age of Reason was still half-baked: Alchemy and mysticism coexisted comfortably with cutting-edge research, often promoted by the same practitioners.

Navigation was a pressing concern for the inhabitants of that island nation. While latitude was (and is) easy to determine— you need only measure the height of the sun from the horizon at noon—longitude was far trickier. For east-to-west estimations at sea, mariners used the appropriately named *dead reckoning*, a technique for extrapolating from their presumed velocity. Not surprisingly, frequent errors led to shipwrecks, with the accompanying loss of life and wealth.

A more accurate reckoning of longitude involved carrying an on-board clock, set to the local time of the port of departure. Comparing that clock's home time with the sun's time gave the navigator the east-to-west distance that had been traversed—provided he knew the latitude. A difference of four minutes between home and local time meant the ship had sailed 1 degree of longitude (up to seventy miles, depending on latitude). But no contemporary clock could come near to that accuracy, where a minute's loss or gain over a month-long voyage could set a ship a dozen miles off course. When the ship got to the point on the map where land should be, the shore would be farther than the horizon, or the ship would have smashed into the rocks.

The Italian astronomer Galileo Galilei had speculated about using a pendulum to determine longitude after his insight that the pendulum's motion was *isochronous*, meaning that the same amount of time passed between ticks regardless of the length of the pendulum's arc. A perhaps apocryphal story tells of Galileo comparing a swinging lamp with another rough timekeeper: his own pulse.

Time measurement, always a source of fascination for inventors, became a political hot-button issue with the ruin of many of King Charles II's naval and trading ships. In the same way that Arctic researchers of all stripes highlight the buzzword "sovereignty" to get their nation's attention and funding, King Charles's subjects assured him that with his patronage they could solve the problem of longitude.

The king established a national observatory at Greenwich in 1675 and commissioned Christopher Wren to design it. If a clock, which at that time meant a very fallible pendulum, could not guide mariners, perhaps a detailed rendering of the sky's changing layout could act as a portable clock. The moons of Jupiter function as a reliable celestial timepiece, but the telescope required to see them doesn't—at least not on a ship on a heaving sea. The Royal Observatory, on a hill in the king's parklands, was set up to predict the moon's position among the stars. In the Great Star Room, two Tompion clocks swung their thirteen-foot-long pendulums side by side. Even these, the most accurate of their time, were sensitive to dust and fluctuations of temperature, and they lost or gained a minute every few days. For ships in the tempestuous seafaring environment, such contraptions were hopeless.

The stakes were raised in 1707 when two thousand souls were lost in a four-ship wreck near Cornwall. Parliament voted to establish a Board of Longitude. Like today's X Prize Foundation, which offers incentives for innovative solutions to humanity's challenges, the Board of Longitude set a prize of more than a million present-day dollars to be awarded to any man who could sail from England to the West Indies—a journey that took months—while keeping to Greenwich Mean Time within two minutes or otherwise determining longitude at sea within half a degree.

The sextant, a newly invented device, became available and proved handy: With it, a mariner could use the moon's position between the sun and stars as a clock hand and divine the time by referring to a nautical almanac. Unfortunately, this method required clear skies. Two more generations passed, and the problem was not yet solved.

The Board of Longitude was so fixated on an astronomical solution to the problem that when a mechanical one came along, they were loath to recognize it. John Harrison's marine chronometer beat the pulse of the universe in the palm of your hand. Even the first version—with four dials, wooden gears and duelling pendulums set to two-second swings—was accurate enough to satisfy the royal benchmark of half a longitudinal degree at sea. The Board reluctantly shelled out a stingy half of the prize money.

Harrison continued to develop his chronometer, subbing in brass and steel parts and amping up the period to five beats per second. Three times more accurate than the initial prototype, his fourth model became standard issue for the navy. It was only six inches in diameter, with a bimetallic strip that compensated for temperature change (a crucial part of all biological clocks, as well). We would recognize it as the earliest incarnation of a pocket watch.

Quite apart from its significance to nautical navigation, the unprecedented accuracy of Harrison's invention brought timekeeping to a threshold that approached Newton's ideal concept: time without beginning or end. Harrison's chronometer, which gained or lost only a fraction of a second per day, existed in the realm of mathematical, inhuman time, uninfluenced by human actions or human heartbeats. Such close contact with Newtonian time was a step toward key scientific concepts of the age—geological time (on a scale far beyond the human lifespan) and its sibling, evolutionary time, which underpinned Darwin's ideas. And from a purely mechanical standpoint, the chronometer pioneered the use of interchangeable parts, which would redefine convenience and efficiency in the new age of the factory.

Clock technology has advanced far beyond the point where it could constitute the bottleneck in any human endeavour. Even our most cheapo watches are more accurate than Harrison's expensive and exclusive chronometer, using vibrating quartz crystals as oscillators in place of pendulums. The most sacred keepers of time, our atomic clocks, are less erratic even than the Earth's slowing rotation itself, which once defined our notion of time. Now time is defined, according to convention, by radiation during state transitions in a Caesium 133 atom at 0 degrees Kelvin.

Time as a concept is so abstract that it's no wonder there's a wide variety of cultural ideations around it. According to experimental psychology, the present as perceived by the brain lasts three seconds. Even though we tell stories as if they flow seamlessly from one moment to the next, our consciousness is, in reality, fragmented. This helps us to react to changes in the environment, giving us a new scenario to work with as events unfold. Think of the hunter who follows a mental plan while failing to notice his prey zigging instead of zagging. The present moment feels fresh and allows for creativity and contingent decisions.

We have clocks everywhere in our urban lives precisely because there's no other way to tell the time. Skyscrapers and the rest of the cityscape obscure the horizon and its information on sun position and future weather conditions. Inside it's always mid-afternoon in late spring. But for cultures living with nature all around them, calendars are based on animal behaviours and ripening fruits. Nature serves as the most accessible clock in history. Traditional Balinese time, for example, isn't even measured quantitatively—

their calendar classifies months by what kind of time it is qualitatively, based on natural phenomena.

Commonalities do emerge, though, in cultural time measurement. Most societies break up time into weeks: blocks of anywhere from three to sixteen days. Our seven-day week, entrenched by Judeo-Christian texts, was invented by the Babylonians, but it's not uncommon to find tides at the base of long-term scheduling. Etymologically linked to *time*, *tide* shows up in words like *Eastertide* or *noontide*. Even if weeks are based on lunar cycles, most cultures use solar cycles to determine years, fitting the moon's phases under a roughly 365-day umbrella.

Time measurement also springs from the human world, from how the day is broken up into activities. In Sudan, the Nuer people are cowherds and tell the time according to the day's work schedule. The clock might read "milking time," "pasturing time" or "cattle-moving time." According to anthropologist Wade Davis, Borneo's Penan people measure time according to subjective perception. If a hunting trip yields a lot of meat, it's understood to have taken a shorter time, even though it may have lasted several days. Brings new meaning to the saying "Time flies when you're having fun."

SEVEN

the bell tolls for thee

Look to the Classical traditions and you'll see that circadian rhythms are covered by a wide range of mythology. Like the legends of most cultures, Greek legends associated sleep with death (for obvious reasons—the sleeping body is inert, the sleeping brain unconscious, and so on). So Thanatos, the Greek god of death, has a younger brother named Hypnos, god of sleep, and another brother named Oneiroi, patron god of the tribe of dreams. They are all sons of Nyx, who represents night. Their other siblings, Eris and Maros, rule over discord and doom, a clue to the early experience of nocturnal life. Chronos, the god of time, might seem a perfect fit for the field of chronobiology, but the better choice, the one that gets to the heart of the matter, is Caerus.

Rather than sequential or chronological time, Caerus represented timing, or the opportune moment; his Roman equivalent was Occasio. Caerus has a lock of hair on his forehead to be grasped when he arrives, as an opportunity, before he can pass by—a sort of *carpe diem* concept—and the back of his head is bald. No man running after him can grab his hair, for the moment has already passed. A great facilitator of thieves and lovers, Caerus has winged feet that carry a fleeting advantage to be seized by opportunists.

The spirit of Caerus is the crux of evolution's perfection of circadian rhythms. For each biological process, there is an opportune instant when the world around colludes with the organism. The sun at its apex can best warm a reptile, and the air in darkness keeps sensitive cells safe from UV rays. The individual that can catch that instant, by way of internal clocks or external cues, will expend less effort to eat, procreate, rest or detoxify—and will do so more successfully. It will, in other words, be fitter as a life form than its compatriots and, on average, leave more copies of itself that carry its superior talents.

This is the evolutionary heritage that led to our body clock, and it's a constant across our species. But each civilization through history has run with it in a unique way. Each has found a way to satisfy or resist the body's needs in keeping with the local conditions and surrounding value systems. The body's timekeeping systems have become a major driver for culture, and there's incredible diversity in how societies respond to it in their attitudes toward sleep, work and other activities.

Caerus's brother Thanatos shows another aspect of our relationship with time. Our self-awareness as a species leads us to impose a sense of order on the forward motion of time. We discern from the patterns around us that we live and die within set time parameters, and we come to understand our own mortality. Each lifetime is parsed into thousands of days, and we obsessively count and recount our remaining allotment on calendars, their grids of little squares cast over time like a net. Psychologist Ernest Becker has proposed that much of what motivates our greatest strivings as humans, as well as our daily actions, is a denial of death. As a defence mechanism against the conscious thought of our own mortality—and the overwhelming anxiety it would cause us—we spend our energies in pursuit of immortality. Whether it's bearing children, sending pieces of ourselves into the distant future or trying to create lasting works that will live on after our bodies are returned to the earth, we live our lives unconsciously raging against the dying of the light.

Developmental psychologist Erik Erikson argues that we devote a portion of our lives to resolving this crisis. After we form our identities in adolescence and settle down in relationships during early adulthood, we spend our mid-life crises trying to set up a mechanism for leaving a lasting legacy.

For all age groups, the unconscious terror of dying can be demonstrated in some very devious and crafty experimental paradigms. Patriotic Christian Americans hold as sacred the image of the crucifix, on which their saviour suffered cruelly and died, as well as the American flag, a symbol of everything their country means to them. Mark Landau and colleagues at the University of Kansas set student subjects up with a nail, a crucifix and various irrelevant objects to imply multiple options in completing their task, which is to hang the crucifix on the wall. The only practicable solution to the problem is to hammer the nail into the wall with the hard, durable crucifix itself, using it as a mere object or tool.

The experimenters also designed a scenario in which black-dyed sand was presented, and test subjects were tasked with removing the dye. The only object on hand that could be used as a filter for washing the sand was an American flag. In this paradigm, the stars and stripes would have to be soiled to complete the assignment.

In both instances, a control group of subjects was assigned to these tasks, and an experimental group was reminded of their own deaths in some way before the tasks began. Subjects reminded of their own impending death took twice as long trying alternatives or else refused entirely to desecrate the flag or crucifix to complete their task.

A *memento mori*, or death reminder, is part of the Christian tradition as a guard against sin. The thinking was that by focusing on the afterlife, rather than on earthly pleasures, pride and other hollow enterprises, people would be consistently aware of mortality. Be it a visit to the cemetery, a grim reaper motif on a church tableau, a skull, a skeleton or a snuffed candle, such themes were seen until recently as wholesome fare. Public clocks carried mottos such as "Perhaps the last hour." The studies just described, with the crucifix and the flag, demonstrate that this approach really does work, if the purpose is to make people cling to their most cherished beliefs. More worrying is that, on another test, they also demonstrated racism, which suggests they are more motivated to protect their in-group—be it their country, their religion or their ethnicity—from anyone they see as "other." Our collective drive to push our culture onto other people might come from a fear of collective, cultural death; the studies above indicate the impulse to impose our culture on others is stronger when we're under threat.

Like just about everyone else I know, I do the same thing every morning before I'm even fully conscious. It's not stretching my arms or yawning or testing the air temperature with my toe. No, my morning routine begins with a glance at the clock—whether it's beeping maliciously at me or not. It's been argued that the Industrial Revolution was triggered not by the invention of the steam engine, but by the widespread adoption of the clock.

The minute madness began in the medieval monastery, where routine and regimentation was prized as a path to godliness. Bells rang at predetermined intervals to signal mealtimes, prayer times, wake times and farming times, and the general idea was to make a big show of order and synchronicity. Though the Benedictine monks had been using primitive timekeeping for this purpose since the sixth century, the mechanical clock, invented in the thirteenth century, leant authority to the imposed schedules. If people didn't sleep when drowsy but rather disciplined their sin-prone bodies into a hurried itinerary of study and work, all the better to prevent idle hands from doing the devil's work.

The fetish for timetables spread to military life and from there to the counting house. In 1370, the German city of Cologne mounted a clock in the town square. The public's perception of time changed so dramatically that, four years later, there were laws enacted around the clock's readings. The workday was to start and end at a specific time, and lunch breaks were to last precisely one hour.

By the sixteenth century, a clock could parse the day into thousands of seconds and had come to represent a piece of machinery whose product was a stream of time units. The accompanying cultural transformation, however, was already well under way—humans, in their quest for regularity, had themselves become mechanical. It was a transition that laid the groundwork for the

BELLS WITH A CAUSE

While the original purpose of church bells was to summon the faithful to prayer, they soon were used for other purposes. Bell-ringers alerted the community to emergencies such as an imminent attack in times of war or a fire in peacetime. Bells also rang out to celebrate a wedding or a hero's return.

The Open Churches Trust, founded by Andrew Lloyd Webber to promote the opening to the public of many of the United Kingdom's churches that are locked between services, organized Celebration 2000 for the millennial New Year's Eve. The goal was to have every church tower in the realm ring in the new year. The hitch was that more than a thousand churches had no bell ringers anymore, so starting in 1997, around five thousand rookies were recruited and trained in the dying art.

time-obsessed Industrial Revolution, when men moulded themselves to the rhythms of their machinery.

In the factory and on the railroads, people marched in step to precisely timed schedules. Their responsiveness to their bodies—knowing to consume meals on a recently empty stomach, for example—was dulled. Initially a means of coordinating transportation and uninterrupted production, the synchronized timetable soon begot a cult of speed and efficiency.

A synchronized global schedule may be a boon for modern industry, but for religions in which punctuality pleases God, universal agreement on time is essential. Islam requires five daily prayers, preferably in congregation at a mosque. In the fourth Sora of the Quran, five prayer times—dawn, noon, afternoon, sunset and night—are defined by qualities of the sunlight.

Vivid descriptions of the red glow of twilight guide the faithful in their rhythmic unfurling of prayer mats. It's particularly useful for those living around Medina or Mecca, where the sharia law was written. A muezzin perched in a minaret, poised to give the call to prayer, can discern the exact moment when no portion of the sun is visible above a horizon unobscured by skyscrapers.

Still, with a history of sophisticated astronomical measurement developed to establish Mecca's exact direction from any given point, Islam isn't fazed by urban locations. The Muslims I know type their home cities into a website and receive a convenient printout of prayer times on a given day—Islam on the go.

But what about at the highest latitudes, where the sun mightn't set for weeks and dusk could follow dawn by a few minutes? Surely followers of the world's fastest-growing religion wouldn't starve during an ill-timed Ramadan, but the holy month could see Muslims waiting for a mythical sunset before breaking their fast if they followed their faith's tenets to the letter.

On a dark November afternoon in Canada's Northwest Territories, I visit Yellowknife's Islamic Centre to see how they cope with the problem. I tromp through the snow to the converted daycare that serves as a mosque and part-time Islamic classroom. It's a step up from the public library where Muslims had to make do with a back room for prayer a few years ago. Then again, the community has grown since then too. The North has attracted Sudanese, Somali and Lebanese men with an expertise in diamond-cutting—or just a good eye for a labour shortage. Now Muslims number almost two hundred out of the city's less than twenty-thousand-strong population.

While I kick off my slushy shoes in the unmarked mudroom full of Sorel workboots, I hear a distant singing of verses and realize I've arrived at prayer time. I sit it out in a cloakroom, not wanting to disturb the worship, happy it isn't a Friday, when the prayers would far outlast their weekday fifteen-minute average. The walls across from me sport an array of clocks, of the Tokyo–Paris–London variety found in stockbrokers' offices. I can't read the Arabic place names beneath.

A large green chalkboard displays a chart of the day's prayer times, with, for each, a call to prayer slotted in ten minutes earlier. In a small community like this, the call is given in the prayer room itself, not broadcast by loudspeaker or over the radio as it is in the Middle East. The Yellowknife members rotate the calling duty among themselves. Tonight's sunset prayer time is listed as 6:25 P.M., but the sun has long since set.

When it sounds like the action is over, I pad down the hallway, stocking feet luxuriating in the thick patterned carpets lining the way. The first couple of men emerging from the mosque meet my eyes with a deer-in-the-headlights look, startled to find their familiar group invaded by a blond, lost-looking lady. I tell them I'm looking for Abdalla, the scholar.

"Yes, we'll get him, but you must wait in there." They point to a closed cubicle in the corner constructed out of office dividers. The women's section.

I squeeze my frame through the narrow entrance and sit in the women's area to wait some more. Deserted and clinical, the cubicle doesn't seem to get much use—perhaps because women pray at the mosque only on special occasions or during Ramadan, but probably because of the lack of Muslim women here. Males vastly outnumber females, and it's reached the point where the group will pool funds to help bring their fiancées to Canada and redress the imbalance, sometimes ponying up as much as $10,000 for immigration costs.

Abdalla Daebes wears a white cap, tannish-grey gown and white socks. He appears to be in his early thirties and wears a wedding ring. He's been the imam here in the Subarctic for six months now, having arrived from Egypt with little preparation and less English. He's come in with a Somali man whom he indicates he will use as a translator. But just as we're settling in and making introductions, a Sudanese taxi driver pops his head into the cubicle, and the translation duties are passed to him instead. "His English is much better—very good," says my former Arabic decoder. "Shut up, she'll find out the truth in a minute," replies his replacement. Adil Idris sits between me and Abdalla, ready for my questions.

Trouble is, he's not much for translating. "It's November 20, and the sun set hours ago, but here you are praying at six in the evening ..." I prompt. Adil explains that when night and day don't cooperate with practicality—near the summer and winter solstices—the Islamic Centre adopts Edmonton prayer times. It's the nearest centre to the south that shares a time zone but enjoys more moderate sunlight hours. "The rest of the time we follow the Yellowknife schedule," he says. Abdalla interjects softly in Arabic. "We are always on Edmonton time all year," amends Adil. "We pray according to what the prophet Mohammed has taught us," he adds cryptically.

Some clerics argue that the sun's high and low points can still be calculated even in perpetual darkness, it's just that the two points both occur below the horizon. It amounts to an evenly spaced five prayers over twenty-four hours, anchored at noon and midnight. "You should be on time," stresses Adil. "For example, this morning, I woke up late and then I prayed, but it's not good. It's important to be on time." I point out that Mohammed had no precise clocks and that his teachings were instead quite specific about sunlight.

I fear Abdalla, the real authority on Islamic scholarship here, has been missing most of the discussion, so I appeal directly to him. In Egypt you prayed in rhythms with the sun, as Mohammed described, I fished. How does it feel here to watch the sun go down with no prayer to acknowledge it? Abdalla responds in a way Adil can't accept. They spend the next five minutes in rapid negotiations over Qurannic teachings, and I see the spirit of debate is alive and well in Canadian Islam.

Finally, an answer for me in English: Mohammed didn't have clocks, so he used the language of the sun's movement to describe these clock times, which were what he was really getting at. Since the invention of the mechanical clock, Muslims have adopted modern time. Prayer times are defined by the clock.

I could buy the line about modernity if there weren't so many mental gymnastics performed throughout the world to calibrate those prayer times to the sun. Painstaking calculations go into triangulating locations with schedules, and various methods are put forward by different institutions, such as the Egyptian Authority of Survey, under the Shafi'i Juristic School.

Abdalla was careful to point out that praying five times a day doesn't translate into a life of incessant prayer. Hard work is an important element of the religion, and Muslims are able to compete in global industry despite the periodic interruptions of their religious duties.

It's been eye-opening to realize that circadian rhythms aren't just spread outward from the centre of global dominant culture. Indeed, wherever ideas about right living are transmitted, there are schedules to accompany them. But Islam's assumptions run up against an environmental stumbling point past a certain latitude.

In the end, though, it's left up to the local religious authorities, and the ones in Yellowknife have come to a compromise with the exacting requirements of their religion. I get a ride home in Adil's cab.

EIGHT

rhythms of the mind

In the Christian tradition, the Lord gave day to the living and night to the dead. The endless night of a far northern winter can feel uninhabitable, and it's what keeps most Southerners away— that and the cold. My first winter in the Northwest Territories was nightmarish. Starting around February, I avoided mirrors. That puffy, pallid skin wasn't mine, it belonged to some cave-dwelling creature. My problem wasn't the bitter cold; in fact, some days I wished my office building had windows that opened for a minus-30 blast of alertness. No, it had everything to do with the darkness that had descended on Yellowknife. Propping my eyelids open with finger and thumb, I crawled through each day. At work I would lean against my desk like a drunkard, steadying myself on my elbows, then on my upper arms, and finally succumbing to the weight of my head and closing my eyes. Needless to say, my job suffered, and I spent my precious waking hours reflecting on how incredibly lazy I was.

It wasn't until the first bright spring afternoon that euphoria struck. I was freed from darkness's grip and realized I hadn't been alone—many of my neighbours and co-workers had been in the same boat all along. In 1984, psychiatrists invented a term for a collection of symptoms suffered during the winter dimness. Sleepiness in daytime, irritability, weight gain and loss of interest in social activities were lumped into an umbrella diagnosis called *seasonal affective disorder* (SAD).

Dr. Ewan Affleck, medical director of the Yellowknife Health and Social Services Authority, is part of the first line of defence for the one quarter of Northerners who suffer a mild case of SAD; severe cases are referred to psychiatrists. Seasonal affective disorder's incidence climbs with latitude. When I tell Affleck I'm interested in seasonal affective disorder, he lets out a long, groaning sigh and moans, "No, not today." It seems like I got off on the wrong foot with him. I ask if it's a bad time right now. He doesn't miss a beat. "It's a horrible time. I'm sorry I can't talk to you, I'm too depressed. The days are getting shorter and there's no light outside. Ohhh!" Sometimes people really have to ham it up to penetrate my gullibility. "It's hard to quantify how much SAD contributes, but anecdotally, you question it," says Dr. Affleck. "We don't treat it as a separate condition. It's a subset of recurring depression. The difference is, it's triggered by fall." The long winters are thought to disrupt normal cycles of melatonin. Normally the onset of daylight inhibits melatonin production, but in the continuous darkness of winter, excessive daytime amounts of melatonin are produced, causing sleepiness throughout the day.

Though SAD can apparently strike anyone at any time, scientists have pinpointed certain factors that increase the risk—age, for instance: SAD strikes at age twenty-three, on average, and the risk of suffering from it increases over a lifetime. The problem is slightly heritable and almost every clinical study finds more of it in women, possibly because of circadian disruption of menstrual cycles. Mostly though, seasonal mood patterns depend on how close you live to the Earth's poles. "There's evidence that as one moves farther north, there's more SAD. Of course it could just be that South Americans are happy, whereas Swedes are naturally morose and boring," Affleck jokes.

While mood changes may be the most noticeable symptom of the effect of extreme latitudes on humans, without roughly equal stretches of alternating sunlight and darkness, our bodies suffer a number of other glitches. Vitamin D is essential for healthy bones and teeth, and it's been shown that regular supplements can increase life expectancy by a year or two. What dairy products don't provide, the skin manufactures with sun exposure. Northerners stock up with a glut of it in summer, but supplies dwindle quickly. "After your shadow is longer than you are, the weak sunlight makes your vitamin D production negligible," says Affleck. "It's been linked to all sorts of disorders, including some cancers." Public health experts call for supplements during the lean times.

Sleep deprivation is a common complaint in the northern summer when the days are endless, and Affleck discounts the theory that people who grew up in the North have less trouble with it. "It varies from person to person," he says. "Some people can fall asleep in a room with the lights on, but others need total darkness." Though poorly understood, there is also a correlation between multiple sclerosis and latitude, he notes. "We see more of it as you get farther north."

A number of measures can be taken to reduce the impact of latitude on health. One approach to the problem involves providing bright artificial light in the home or workplace. Research shows regular sessions of artificial sunlight, including a simulated dawn in the morning, tends to alleviate symptoms within a couple of weeks. Affleck doesn't always have the benefit of follow-up with his patients, so he cannot easily assess the efficacy of these treatments from his own clinical experience. "I've stuck people in front of SAD lamps before. Sometimes you hear of people getting headaches from them," he says.

Veterans of life in the far north almost all agree on the best way to deal with winter gloom. Northwest Territories' former premier Joe Handley, for example, joins the chorus advising sufferers to stay active. Living off the grid—a quintessentially Northern life-style—on Prelude Lake near Yellowknife, Joe and his family enjoy a steady supply of solar power for their waterfront estate during summer, but they welcome winter's descent. "I grew up always active on a farm in Saskatchewan, so it's second nature for me to get outside when I can," Joe explains.

Though the wood stove in his house needs constant stoking and the generators need refuelling, Handley has a smaller cabin in the woods as an even more rustic and remote getaway. Before the winter blues catch up to him, he'll hop on a Ski-Doo and fly along the trails for forty minutes to outrun them, taking in the scenery's glittering, frosty beauty as preventive medicine. "I find the people who stay inside and complain about the cold are always the ones who have a hard time of it with seasonal depression and that. You have to force yourself to get out there," he says. "Unless it's 40 below with the wind really howling." Moderation in stoicism, as in everything. There's a limit to how much cold even a Northerner willingly endures.

Exposure to full-spectrum lighting—the kind that best imitates the sun—can be not only a cure but also an effective prevent-ive measure. Stanton Territorial Hospital in Yellowknife, where doctors and nurses cope with long hours and shift work, made the switch to full-spectrum bulbs in some areas of the build-ing, citing worker protection. In some ways, the shift work itself becomes easier near the winter and summer solstices when there are no competing cues from sunlight to contradict the artificial sleeping schedule.

Some critics/health professionals believe more dramatic meas-ures should be introduced, such as longer lunch hours during the winter months so people can take advantage of the brief window when the sun is up. Nice idea, but unlikely to be implemented any time soon.

In modern society, we don't slow down to accommodate these seasonal changes. Though longer nights make for more melatonin release in general—with accompanying fatigue and a decrease in overall activity, leading to weight gain—we act as oblivious as possible under the circumstances.

In Britain, at a latitude of 51 degrees north, the prevalence of SAD is around 3 percent of the total population in winter whereas more than a quarter of residents in Tromsø, Norway, at a latitude of 69 degrees north, suffer from its effects. But you don't have to be in a polar region to worry about darkness and its influence on the mind. Even in California, where the sun famously shines on everyone, people are indoors so much of the time that they typically see less than two hours of sunlight a day. With age, this exposure decreases steadily—particularly in females—with healthy women over fifty getting only twenty minutes of natural light per day. Winter can mean a few pounds of weight gain and general sluggishness even if it doesn't progress into full-fledged diagnosable pathology. Slowing down and conserving energy might even be a remnant of a natural coping strategy. Even if we don't actually hibernate, sleeping a lot and craving carbohydrates—though associated with depression—could mean the difference between life and death through a cold month in the wild. If we have first rested and fattened up, we would be more likely to survive.

A problem less common than SAD, though equally seasonal, is that of summer mania. In roughly a fifth of bipolar patients, depressive episodes can congregate in winter and manic ones in summer, and there's something about the longer days that seems to trigger mania even in non-bipolar people. Hospitalizations for depression peak in late fall, whereas those for mania peak in summer. Mania's number-one sign is little sleep paired with lots of energy. Rapid speech and excessive socializing are other giveaways. A normal boost in mood that goes along with lots of bright light exposure in spring can trigger a cascade of chemical changes that gets out of hand very quickly. The treatment window for mania is much shorter than for depression, so prevention—sometimes in the form of dark glasses and equivalent behavioural changes—is critical.

Having established that human bodies are ruled by the planet's rotation, we now know that our minds are not immune to the effects of a rising and setting sun. In Basel, Switzerland, psychiatrist Anna Wirz-Justice created an artistic demonstration of this. She calls it *The Melatonin Room*. Designed around hormone stimulation, the exhibit eliminates sleepiness in visitors through a specific wavelength of green light, and then makes them tired again, using UV rays. Wirz-Justice's early work on seasonal affective disorder led to the most common treatment today, the SAD lamp. At least 2,500 lux for a critical period from three thirty to eight in the morning has been shown effective in alleviating symptoms, especially for milder, subclinical cases.

The mind and the body clock work reciprocally. Just as disrupting circadian rhythms can lead to depression, so psychological problems can interfere with a healthy body clock, through the action of hormones. Any number of modern lifestyle factors is implicated.

Chronic stress from bad eating, sedentary living and isolation can flatten out circadian curves so that true wakefulness never fully emerges in the daytime and sleep is never deep. Along with long work hours come elevated adrenaline and cortisol levels, a recipe for insomnia—not to mention heart disease and diabetes. Disturbance in sleeping rhythms is often the first sign that something is wrong in the body. Schizophrenic patients complain of irregularities in their body clock, and monitoring hormonal levels confirms it.

An unsung substance in the sleep world, the hormone *prolactin* is generally associated with breastfeeding and orgasm (and rightly so), but it's also released in great quantities during sleep, especially during the REM sleep toward the end of the night. Among its many functions, prolactin is responsible for relaxation, dampening down sex hormones.

High cortisol levels pose problems for flight attendants, who release cortisol at all hours of the day because of jet lag. It's very worrying to see the memory problems and cognitive impairment that go along with this job: The thought is that cortisol's unrelenting presence actually damages the brain over time. The more we know about cortisol, the more it becomes apparent that preventing and relieving stress is a vital health skill—to keep the body's internal processes and daily rhythms on an even keel.

As a coping mechanism, music can be calming, as can meditation, but for most of us our friends are the great stress relievers. Through their social support and companionship—not to mention a good laugh—our blood pressure is reduced and mood-lifting endorphins start to flow. In the long run, though, it's best not to create that stress in the first place.

The feeling of control over your destiny trumps any other factor in managing stress. What psychologists call your *locus of control* can be either internal or external. You either attribute your fate to the world around you—falling into a depressive state of learned helplessness when presumably uncontrollable disasters occur—or you believe you have the power to change life's outcomes. Health psychologists have found the internal attributional style to be predictive of successful control of diabetes, obesity and other conditions that demand vigilance and self-discipline. The world is a much more stressful place for those who believe themselves to be pawns of the elements. In experiments whose subjects believe they are controlling the administration of a painful stimulus using a dummy set of levers, levels of inflammatory cortisol—harmful in the long term—are lower than in conditions where the subjects merely receive the same painful stimuli. Believe that your actions make a difference to your future, and your body will relax.

Early hunter-gatherers walked up to eighteen kilometres a day and ran long distances, too. After just half an hour of exercise, mood brightens for a good part of the day and stress is held at bay. It should be enough to combat the negative stress effects on circadian hormones as well, as the endorphins start to flow and cortisol eases. Sleep patterns improve with exercise, deepening and lengthening natural sleep. It's possible this is related to the light that goes hand in hand with exercise outside. While waking time is by definition more physically active than sleeping time, a tight correlation actually binds short sleep time with obesity, suggesting society-wide sleep deprivation could have a large role in the obesity epidemic.

So many of the original circadian researchers were German that much of the terminology in the field is borrowed from their language. Thus our sense of time is called *zeitgedaechtnis*, from the German word for "memory of time" and time cues are *zeitgebers*, meaning "time-givers" or "synchronizers." The former is our felt time—something that passes more slowly under the influence of, say, cannabis or general inactivity, but speeds up with, say, alcohol or codeine. Humans, being self-aware, experience time subjectively. An accurate circadian system does not necessarily mean an accurate sense of time, however, and people can sometimes wildly miss the mark when tested for their time perception.

Studies investigating the human ability to estimate time have uncovered two separate systems, one for short-interval and the other for long-interval estimation. Pressing a button after a minute has elapsed is a different sort of task than judging how many days have elapsed while alone in an isolation room, as in the cases of the long-term bunker experiments we saw earlier. Over a period of months with no time cues, isolated people can experience bicircadian rhythms—twice the usual length of a circadian rhythm—and the passage of roughly two days or forty-eight hours is experienced as one day. The fact that the subjects are completely unaware of the extraordinary length of the day suggests that their subjective perceptions of time are tied to their internal rhythms. By definition, then, the body and mind's subjective day is one complete sleep-wake cycle, no matter how long it lasts on clock time.

Short-interval estimates are less closely tied to circadian free-running rhythms and more subject to influence by factors like body temperature and distraction. If undistracted, we are accurate to 15 percent in judging intervals of seconds, minutes or hours. Subjects asked to estimate time and then given some other task to do at the same time usually overestimate the number of seconds that have passed. Interestingly, a second task added to the mix tends to lead to underestimating the time interval, suggesting the brain was so busy it forgot to count off a few ticks of the internal clock.

"Thee shouldstna sit i' the dark, Mother," says George Eliot's character Adam Bede, "that makes the time seem longer." The time-dilating phenomenon so long recognized in literature was confirmed in the 1960s, but we still don't have a clear idea of what causes it. Aschoff showed that time passes much faster for people in brightly lit places. In two underground isolation units in Andechs, Germany, eighteen of Aschoff's subjects lived in differing levels of illumination for weeks. They were asked to estimate short periods of time—ten or twenty seconds, for example—by pressing the space bar on a computer keyboard when they felt the time had elapsed. In dim light, subjects were premature in their bar-pressing, whereas brightly lit subjects pressed it later, meaning that the seconds passed more quickly in the brightness and felt like less time. Interestingly, depressed people tend to produce longer objective intervals for a given subjective time period. Add time memory to the equation—ask someone how long yesterday's power outage lasted, for example—and the answer will typically be useless. It would seem we use a non-circadian timing system for time-estimation tasks and have no conscious access to our own body clocks.

The other German term *zeitgeber* refers to anything that can reset the body clock by hinting at the time outside. In everyday situations, light is the strongest *zeitgeber*, particularly full-spectrum light that mimics—or comes from—the sun. It is a strong indication that the time falls between 6 A.M. and 6 P.M., on average, and if the circadian clock is reading a different hour, it should reset itself. Though there is a lot of anatomy dedicated to this light-as-*zeitgeber* system, with a direct neural pathway linking the retina to the SCN, illumination is not the only way to influence our body clocks.

During the late nineteenth century, Ivan Pavlov investigated his famous dogs' sense of time using conditioning techniques. "I am convinced," he wrote, "that directly along this path of exact experimentation lies the solution of the problem of time, which has occupied philosophers for countless generations." If a dog were given food every thirty minutes, it would start drooling half an hour after the last feeding. Similarly, it could be trained to salivate three minutes after a given cue, in the anticipation of food. Eating is a *zeitgeber* for the clocks in our digestive organs. The liver, kidney and pancreas need to prepare for food to come, so they set their clocks to anticipate usual meal times. That's why jet lag often involves an upset stomach—the food caught the gut unawares.

Our human tendency to plan and schedule may arise from our body's preference for predictable events. A full meal, for example, along with the surge of blood sugar that follows it, is actually quite a stressful event for the digestive system. We feel hungry at lunchtime not because we're running low on the fuel we consumed at breakfast, but because we anticipate the approaching lunch hour.

Blood-sugar levels dip to proactively counteract the effects of our lunch, but if we don't eat the expected lunch, they rebound again. Our digestive system evolved to cycle between expecting food, eating and digesting food in the stomach, and then fasting for several hours while the food is absorbed in the intestines. Many people now tend to go straight from eating to the expectancy phase, always anticipating their next meal. If they could only get into the practice of letting their digestion take a rest, their system would become conditioned to it and would no longer cause cravings outside of mealtimes.

As a social species, we like to follow group norms. Much of our learning comes from group interactions, and our rhythms are fine-tuned by what others around us are doing: another *zeitgeber*. Traffic noises give us an indication that it's rush hour, with all the associations of that time of day. Even knowing that it's three o'clock serves as a social signal to calibrate our rhythms and steer us toward the teapot. The days of the week also influence our cycles. Sunday means sleeping in, and our rhythms correspondingly shift our cycles later on weekends, followed by a jarring Monday morning alarm clock. Social synchrony promotes cohesiveness, and we often tailor our timetables to those of family and friends. We may wait for a while after our stomachs have sounded the lunch alarm, just to be able to accompany a friend to a restaurant. If we're up late at night when the world is sleeping, we may find ourselves at loose ends and turn in as well, from boredom as much as from sleepiness. Rodents and lizards use their circadian systems socially too—the dominant status of certain members of the group places them in a temporal niche related to the group such that certain times of day are for animals lower in the hierarchy to be active and other times are for the higher-status individuals. Rats are generally nocturnal, and the dominant rats will deny lower-ranking individuals access to food sources at night, so the socially low-ranked rats can often be found foraging during the daytime.

❦

The mind and the body clock interact, feeding information to each other. Just as psychological and social cues about time of day can influence our circadian rhythms, so our minds also try to interpret the internal-time information flowing outward from our biological clock. New directions in body-clock research point to various mechanisms we have for estimating time intervals.

If you ask someone to tell you when ten seconds have elapsed, starting ... now, their answer will depend on their body temperature. A higher body temperature will speed up whatever chemical clock we use to count off subjective seconds; it stands to reason because heat generally speeds up chemical reactions. Even a technique such as mentally rehearsing "One, one thousand, two, one thousand" or "One Mississippi, two Mississippi," and so on, can be affected by speeding up those thoughts and making them seem like a longer time period. Biologically, more happened during that time, so, for all intents and purposes, it was a longer time period, or so says our mind.

This holds true for estimating intervals of five or ten seconds, but it turns out there's no body-temperature effect at all on guesses of an hour-long period. Tell someone to press a button the moment they think an hour has passed, and their answer has nothing to do with body temperature and everything to do with when they woke up in the morning. Subjective hours are longer for those who woke up later—that is, more recently. This suggests to me that people are trying to gauge hours by chunking their day into fractions, starting with when they woke up.

Though this book deals with different cultures around the world as being biologically identical as far as circadian rhythms are concerned, there have been some population studies on whether our body clocks vary. We know, for example, that there are several forms our clock genes can take and that a few variants are represented within a population. Clock genes code for proteins that vary rhythmically in concentration. When transcription factors are released in response to low clock-protein levels, the proteins are assembled, and they peak in concentration in the wee hours of night before being broken down by enzymes to start the cycle again. The levels of these proteins are the basis of circadian time, and the type of clock gene you inherit can affect whether you are a morning or an evening person and how strongly your body clock affects you.

The frequency of each type of gene has, in fact, been found to vary significantly from the Ghanaian to the Han Chinese and Papua New Guineans; however, when all the data are analyzed, it appears that genetic drift is the cause of these differences. A group of people sharing the same genetic profile living more or less cut off from other groups of people will, over time, develop their own genetic peculiarities through random mutation that have nothing to do with natural selection. So the clock genes of different peoples may show subtle differences but function in the same way. In other words, random changes, rather than natural selection, affected the preponderance of any given type of clock gene. So the environmental differences these people experience—their light exposure and latitude—have not changed their body-clock genes, at least the ones we've looked at so far. I take this as confirmation of my approach in treating the body clock as a biological universal, a foundation on which cultures lay their own rituals and rhythms.

As with gravity and magnetism, forces are often discernible only by their effects. Such is the case with the body clock. The hidden forces acting on our biology and behaviour are numerous and their hiddenness comes from the fact that they function perfectly well without input from our cortex. The systems that act to preserve our internal balance and harmonize our bodies with the environment bypass the higher centres of the brain so that our thoughts can be freed up for processing input that requires their attention.

There's a famous demonstration of the brain's communication with itself: The left hemisphere (the most verbally gifted half) and the right hemisphere (which puts an emphasis on visual and spatial skills) are normally collaborating with each other as we go about our daily tasks. A complex of nerves called the *corpus callosum* connects the two halves and sends information back and forth. Some severely epileptic patients have had these nerves surgically cut, however, as a last-ditch attempt to contain their seizures. In general, they still have quite a high degree of functioning, but the effect of the separation of their two brains is revealed in a neat experiment.

One such epileptic, whose corpus callosum had been cut, was seated and told to read some cue cards while the researcher covered one of the epileptic's eyes (counterintuitively, the right eye is primarily connected to the left hemisphere and vice versa). When the subject read with his right eye, he had no trouble saying the words, and he could recall them later, no problem. Then a card was shown to his left eye. It said *Stand up*. He stood up. When asked what had made him stand up, he told the researcher he was just going out to the hall to get a drink, because he was thirsty.

The left side of his brain, not having seen the command, noticed the man was standing up and created a reason for it. People with intact brains also make up explanations for the things we do when we do not have conscious access to the source of those behaviours. Often we react to stimuli we don't consciously notice. In these cases, we fudge a plausible story and move on. Yes, the girl in the hallway might be really, really attractive, but maybe your heart is pounding because you've just run up the stairs and you're out of shape. Often you'll attribute your physical response to the girl, through a subliminal process involving the emotional centres in the brain. We can't always correctly pin down the reasons for our feelings, and sometimes those reasons are as pervasive and subtle as the seasons.

The way our bodies respond to unconscious cues lies behind some of jet lag's cognitive effects. For example, an athlete's psychological preparation for an international meet can be altered if his internal time cues in the country where he competes are inconsistent with the cues he trained with. Quite apart from travel fatigue, the very learning athletes have achieved during training can fly out the window through a phenomenon called state-dependent memory. It's one of the reasons coaches emphasize replicating training conditions on race day.

A university student will perform best on a math exam if the test is in the same classroom where he learned the material. He'll do even better if the exam is scheduled for the same hour of the day as the math class meets. Little cues like the smell of a marker the professor uses or the sounds of the intersection outside can trigger good retrieval of material he learned in that setting.

This is why addictions, another form of learning, can often only be broken with a change in routine or setting. The sight of a smoker buddy can bring back the learned behaviour of lighting up. The smell of a cup of coffee or a sip of beer may have a similar effect upon a social smoker. Anti-addiction programs often seem more effective than they actually are, because the addict is able to clean up quite easily in an in-patient setting, but quickly relapses when back in his old hangouts. The more genuinely effective programs involve exposing the addict to the cues that trigger cravings, preferably the whole environment, without allowing use of the drug of choice. Gradually the addict becomes desensitized to those cues and ceases to associate them with the drug. In much the same way, a triathlete's focused rehearsal of the transition from the pool to the bike can be made smoother depending on the relative familiarity of the setting.

$$\text{⏰}$$

Lifted entirely out of all familiar settings are the residents and visitors at Eureka High Arctic Weather station, the northernmost civilian outpost in the world, on Ellesmere Island, 1,500 kilometres north of the Arctic Circle. With eight permanent staff from Environment Canada, a department of the federal government, the station's meteorologists measure atmospheric conditions as well as terrestrial factors like ice thickness. Follow the winding coast of Ellesmere Island yet farther north and you would come to Alert, the Canadian military base that lays claim to the title for northernmost outpost overall and for which Eureka serves as a communications relay. In a setting where nothing in the environment consistently instructs them about what might be appropriate, the residents must form their own daily schedules.

In March, the month of polar sunrise there, when the sun first comes above the horizon after a dark winter, I hitch a lift to the Eureka station on the fortnightly supply run from Resolute, Nunavut. The scenery is stunning. Icebergs rise out of the two-metre-thick flat ice of the nearby fjord. I go with the Environment Canada team as they drive out onto the ice to perform the daily thickness measurement and release hydrogen balloons into the minus-46-degree air to make atmospheric measurements thirty kilometres above the ground.

A luxurious—given the circumstances—accommodations building houses visiting scientists and eight permanent staff who rotate on three-month shifts. Water is collected in a nearby reservoir and food is flown in. An icebreaker makes a yearly delivery when the island is accessible in summer. Before my arrival, Eureka's tiny community spent its entire three-month stay in total

darkness, getting to know a local pack of Arctic foxes and enjoying one another's company. I have been asked to bring up a bottle
of Scotch to replenish the dwindling liquor supplies at the base—I
bring two, which I share with atmospheric physicists around a pool
table in the rec room, as two graduate students practise Pilates in
the corner and another watches the latest season of *Survivor* on
television. They call this place the Sheraton of the North.

In the sixty years since the weather station was established, it
hasn't always been so cushy. I don a headlamp and bundle up to
explore the old, now-unheated accommodations quarters where
the all-male staff would winter over. The ghost of an insane cook
is said to haunt this building—assaults are not unheard of in such
crazy-making surroundings. Workers gripped by what psychiatrists have dubbed *polar madness* have been known to lash out
violently, though the more common response is depression and
lethargy, basically a severe form of SAD.

It hasn't always been a frigid desert here. A mere 45 million
years ago, Ellesmere Island still had months of perpetual darkness,
but the setting for the hundred-day polar night was a subtropical
wetland. Alligators, horses, tapirs and tortoises shared the landscape with broad-leaved deciduous forest. Many nocturnal
mammals evolved here, primed for warm darkness.

I've arrived to a bustling change from the sleepy station's
norm—polar sunrise is the best time to measure ozone deple-
tion because the sun hasn't been around all winter to replenish
the supply. Researchers at the Polar Environment Atmospheric
Research Laboratory (PEARL), a short drive from the Eureka
weather station, direct their sensor equipment upward to the polar
vortex that circulates the North Pole.

I'm at the 80th parallel and not far away from a longitude of
86 degrees west, a great opportunity to participate in a global
internet initiative called the Degree Confluence Project. Started
on a lark in 1996 by Alex Jarrett, a New Englander intent on
finding a creative use for his new GPS, the project aims to create

an organized sampling of the world: At each latitude and longitude integer degree intersection (there's one within seventy-nine kilometres of you), volunteers submit photos of the scenery and of their Global Positioning System's screen as proof. What strikes me, surfing the database, is the total absence of human development in most of the photos.

A group of us heads out onto the tundra, over steep dunes of hard-packed snow. Though the GPS batteries are feeble in the cold and fade the GPS display almost to vanishing, we make it to the spot, and the moment is made sweeter by a glorious find—nothing for miles around but 40-below winds and pure white snow, but at the very confluence of 80 degrees north and 86 degrees west, an unassuming pot adorns the ground. Inside is a collection of memorabilia, known as a *geocache*, left by visitors past. We sign the logbook and add a few tokens of our own before heading back to the warm glow of a computer screen, where our photos are uploaded to be shared with the rest of the world.

The Earth's daily rotation is only one of the many rhythms in nature that affect human lives. Other rhythmic influences include the phases of the moon and the seasons of the year. While many of the planet's cycles have all-too-real effects on everyday human lives, some perceived effects—alive and well in current and historical folklore—are more in the mind than in reality. As an example, take the many entrenched myths surrounding full-moon effects. Stanton Territorial Hospital is the central medical facility in the Northwest Territories. I visit the second-floor maternity ward, which handles the better part of NWT births. Midwifery is in its infancy here, far behind Europe where it is prevalent, and while there is one midwife who practises within the hospital, home birth is not an option. A group of Inuit teenagers from the Kitikmeot region of Nunavut slowly pace the halls with their labouring friend. Periodically the girl stops her pacing and leans against the wall in a silent contraction. A nurse named Lindsay shows me a labour room, equipped with a shower stall big enough for a woman to be seated in and an exercise ball ideal for bouncing on while the baby makes its way to the birth canal. "There's only three rooms in use right now, but it does get crazy here sometimes—it comes in waves," says Lindsay. "You should see this place on a full moon. We've had people set up in the hallways and three to a room." The nurse across the hall looks up from her charting to roll her eyes, not in dismissal but in corroboration. With the weight of years of experience, medical professionals will tell you a full moon means trouble. Police officers insist their full-moon shifts are an endless series of domestic disputes and street assaults. Psychiatric staff recall increased psychotic behaviour on these nights. Only problem is, the data disagree.

It's true that many creatures on intertidal habitats are ruled by the moon's cycles, as we saw in Chapter 1. The moon has also had a huge influence over human culture since the very earliest lunar calendars. To this day, Easter, for example, is calculated according to the phase of the moon. But study after study has ruled out any biological effect of the moon on humans.

Ask a true believer how the moon could possibly make someone aggressive or give birth or go crazy and they will often blame gravity. The moon's pull drags oceans, after all. On closer examination, this explanation doesn't fly. It's precisely because of the oceans' size that we can see any effect at all—perhaps a few metres in either direction. Perhaps you are reading this from the comfort of your living room couch. The cushions behind you are compressed and your head hovers roughly 15 centimetres from the wall. The wall now exerts more gravitational pull on your head than does the moon. It turns out that gravity is an exceptionally weak force, not worth worrying about unless you are falling. Diligent statisticians have crunched the numbers on a grand scale and determined that there are no significant correlations between the phase of the moon and the following: suicide, absenteeism, conception, birth, menstruation, auto accidents, outpatient admissions, psychosis, depression, anxiety, violent behaviour, heart failure ... the list goes on.

The persistent belief in a moon–madness connection may have been handed down to us in lore from a time when it had some basis in fact, as we saw in Chapter 3. Pre-industrial societies were much more affected by the night's natural lighting conditions. On nights with lunar illumination, they could extend nocturnal activities. Used to sleeping in near-total darkness, however, people would likely have suffered disrupted sleep when the moon shone bright. It's possible this triggered mania and seizures—even partial sleep loss can induce mania in bipolar patients as well as seizures in epileptics. Hence the term *lunacy*.

Seasonality also holds its fair share of psychological effects related to the planet's tilt and journey around the sun. Each year, almost a million people kill themselves, making suicide the thirteenth most common cause of death in the world—ahead of road accidents. It's only getting more common, particularly in young people. Many more millions attempt it every year, creating a huge health-care burden and the untold suffering of loved ones. That's also a lot of statistics to work with, and when the dates are plotted on a graph, a clear seasonal trend emerges. It's not what you might expect. In the northern hemisphere, suicide—particularly violent suicide, by drowning and hanging—peaks in May and June. Studies of Australian deaths confirm this is a summer thing: Their suicides soar in February and have the lowest rates in June. Though crisis centres and help lines are busiest around Christmas, it seems people are less likely to actually go through with their self-harming plans then.

Parsing the possible causes of this mysterious but very robust effect shows just how complex science gets when it comes to societal trends. Summer days are hotter, maybe more sticky and uncomfortable. A person could lose patience more easily under the stress of a hot day and get exasperated with problems he or she would otherwise cope with. But the hotter countries actually show less suicide overall, so we can scratch the hot-and-sticky-weather explanation off the list.

The author of the first convincing study suggested that summer brings with it more socializing, which would lead to more events that might cause suicide—more arguments because there's more talking overall, more breakups because there are more relationship events in total. Others threw in the theory that depressed people may cling to visions of a happy summer to get them through the hard winter. When summer doesn't meet their expectations with genuinely positive life change, it's the last straw.

Two key clues point to an answer. The first is that victims of bipolar disorder and depression are more likely to kill themselves during an upswing after a depressed episode. The theory goes that all the suicidal scheming is at last met with motivation to initiate action. Friends are dumbfounded by a death just as things seemed to be improving. The same goes for antidepressants—there's a short-term increased risk of suicide right at the beginning of treatment as the pharmacology does its work and lifts someone out of a lethargic misery.

The second clue is that the summer-suicide effect is strongly linked to sunlight. If day length has increased markedly in the past few days, an increase in suicides follows. It looks like daylight acts a little like an antidepressant, first empowering us with energy to act on our plans and only later improving our mood.

Even a cursory glance at monthly police statistics in temperate zones confirms that crime soars in the summer months. People gather outside, linger around bars and stage break-and-enters. In the warm summer months, outside feels like inside, and the lack of confinement releases the best and worst elements of human behaviour to the common areas of the city.

Circadian rhythms research progresses with stunning speed in the hard, biological sciences—in botany, zoology and human biology. Psychology is only beginning to apply the body clock to its discipline, and as we progress in this book from the physical sciences to the social ones—history, sociology and anthropology—we make an interdisciplinary link that is barely established in the literature. The few rigorous studies that have uncovered circadian effects on psychology and culture point to a wealth of exciting research directions.

Personality psychologists are trying to make sense of the finding that different chronotypes—morning larks versus night owls—vary along the introversion–extroversion dimension. In this case, the correlation between being outgoing and being a night owl could indicate a number of different forces at work. Being an evening person exposes the night owl to evening culture, with its nightclubs, parties and socializing expectations. On the other hand, being attracted to the social scene motivates extroverts to stay up later, shifting their phase to match their ideal social schedule.

A third factor could be involved, such as a genetic difference that influences both extraversion and nighttime wakefulness. But in biopsychosocial sciences at the moment, interactionism is king. Current psychologists would likely emphasize that there is probably an interaction between two or more of these cause-and-effect relationships. For example, why is it that our culture does the bulk of its socializing after dinner rather than before breakfast? It's a rather arbitrary scheduling choice, but seems to hold up in much of the world; perhaps the underlying biology of gregarious people has played a part in the cultural evolution of this practice.

NINE

mucking around with our circadian cycles

The longest-running job of my youth was at an after-hours night-club. Thursday through Sunday, I sold bottles of water and juice for $4.75 to hordes of sweating partiers long after the club district had shut down. I'd set up my juice bar at a quarter to three in the morning and wedge orange foam plugs into my ears as the first DJ of the shift started his sound check. The grungy basement hall, with its low ceilings and stained couches, hadn't much to recommend it in the harsh fluorescent "ugly lights" of set-up time, but when the room went dark and the black lights glowed purple, a community sprang to life.

The core of the dance-floor population was formed by house music aficionados—some were capping off a night of dancing, but others got up at 5 A.M. to make the regular Sunday pilgrimage to hear our resident DJs. They called it "going to church." Dealers selling GHB, ketamine, ecstasy and coke worked the room's borders, exuding tense business acumen. Gangsters, bikers and prostitutes were among the regulars too. The security team was extensive and top-notch, relatively devoid of the macho power trippers the bouncer profession attracts. A number of them had seen combat and were trained both in martial arts and conflict de-escalation. Every night we needed them. Each shift was a controlled explosion. Far from adhering to a customer-is-always-right service ethos, we made it our daily mission to keep the inmates from running the asylum.

It was difficult to explain to my friends why I adored this job so much. Not only were people with low life prospects slowly killing themselves and each other, but the police would periodically burst in and make essentially random arrests—plus, my paycheques often bounced. But like many before me, I had discovered the self-determination that is possible only at the margins of society. There was none of the cattiness of office politics in this place, and I made more in tips than I've ever made in my salaried positions, before or since.

The floor manager was a Polish ex-boxer named Rudy, after an Uncle Rudolph sent to his death in Siberia. In another life, Rudy had been on the verge of a multi-million-dollar oil contract with Libya when an unfortunately timed embargo scuttled the deal. He showed me his copy of Moammar Gadhafi's *The Green Book*, given to him by the author himself, and described the elite female bodyguards that formed the closest ring of security around Libya's de facto leader.

The hardest part of the job was keeping my eyes open. Everything else over the course of a sixteen-hour double shift was rudimentary in comparison. Inventory had to be taken before and after, and we had to roll the change in our till at the end and square up the cash with the sales, eating the difference if there was a deficit. Rudy would redo the counts, flicking each bill with a practised feel for counterfeit.

After a single shift that had started at midnight, I would climb the steps to the street, eyes squeezed into a squint, as passing commuters made their way into the central business district to start their days. It would take the better part of my walk home to fully open my second eye to the glaring Monday morning sunshine. That very light shifted my circadian system still later, with the message that evening—according to my internal time— had not yet even begun. Neighbours watching my zombie shuffle should have been thankful I had no driver's licence—I wouldn't even have been fit to drive a golf cart. Unlike nine-to-five day workers, my leisure time wasn't a beer after work and staying up in front of the television for five, sometimes six hours after close- of-business. Rather, I caught up with friends in the evening before my shift started, so fatigue had even longer to set in at work, as the hours ticked by long after waking.

Sleep was numb in my windowless bedroom above an Angolan sports bar in Little Portugal, with only the illuminated line of hardwood under the door and the sound of my roommates to tip me off to the time. Weekdays were my free time to read for hours or meet up with friends in Kensington Market and bring our ninety-nine-cent Jamaican patties into the park to eat on the grass. If I was still in nighthawk mode, the university library was open twenty-four hours a day (!) during exam time, but like most night shifters, I tended to adopt the conventional day-active life- style on my days off.

All well and good for a few years of extended adolescence, but for long-term night-shift workers with families, the constant mismatch between internal and external time can be much more stressful. Disruptions are myriad, from telemarketers to noisy traffic. Even one's children going about their day can subtract from precious sleep. Night workers get at least one hour less sleep every day than they would otherwise—a deficit that accumulates through the week—but they still miss out on the social aspects of life. Forget catching the hockey game or following a prime-time show, this segment of the workforce (15 percent in the United States) is lucky if they can fit in quality time with the kids and maintain a relationship. On the plus side, they have access to shops during banking hours and can get out for a hike in the woods while the sun is shining.

Health research has uncovered a variety of ailments endemic to shift work. Independent of weight, smoking and exercise, these employees have about one-third more heart attacks than the general population and many more peptic ulcers and digestive problems. Thinking of the only nearby food source during my "bartending" shifts—a 7-Eleven convenience store with nasty corn dogs decaying under heat lamps and acres of potato chips— I'm not surprised to learn that shift workers tend to eat more junk food. Even if a hearty home-cooked meal were put in front of me at four in the morning, I'm not sure I'd have known what to do with it. Frequent snacking was all I had the appetite for.

The nightclub's security detail tended toward an even more gruelling routine. Igor Ilicin remembers working 104 hours per week for a year and a half. A civil engineer by training, he left Croatia for Canada in his mid-twenties and invested in a house in Toronto's suburbs. He took on security work, both at the after-hours club and at a strip joint, as well as an office job that started at eight in the morning. Waking up four days a week at 7 A.M. and going to sleep at 5 A.M. three nights a week took more and more of a toll as two years turned into five, but for Igor there was pride in paying down the mortgage and securing his place in a city far from his family back in Croatia. Occasionally I'd see him bury his head in his hands at his security post, desperate for sleep.

Finally, in 2010, Igor quit bouncing. "My body has been in constant adjustment mode, tired all the time, and that affected my mood, health, performance," he says. "I was thinking about the body clock for the last few years, but just didn't have the guts to cut my source of income." Toronto's clubbing district had become rougher too. He decided to take the leap when he realized that health and happiness were priceless to him and that he'd prefer to die happy than rich.

Newly energized, he dedicated himself to his budding real estate business with a sideline in personal training. Before many months had elapsed, though, Igor felt a void where nightclub work used to be. He doesn't drink or party, so weekend evenings seemed a little empty—the nightclubs had become his social life, a playground on the clock, but to attend them without a role to play as a member of the staff was a bizarre concept. He struck a deal with a club owner to work just two nights a week as a manager. Without his security shirt on, Igor could more credibly hand out his card as a real estate agent and gain clients. He could also spend social time without anxiety about being unproductive. His new self-employment meant he didn't have to be at an office early in the morning, so daily life wasn't such a struggle against his body.

If we can fly half way around the world and, after a week or two, adjust fully to the twelve-hour time difference, why can't a night worker do the same? It's possible, but the change is slower and more fragile, because so many surrounding cues are in conflict with a night schedule. If a worker joins his daughter at the Little League game on the weekend, he may have to start all over again on Monday's night shift. To make matters worse, shifts are often assigned on a rotating basis.

A round-the-clock production line, command post or power plant typically runs morning, afternoon and night shifts of eight hours each. Swing shifters, who might work a week of nights followed by a week of days, have a higher incidence of certain cancers and live as if chronically jet lagged. The point of swing shifts, and the reason they're so popular with the unions, is that they give workers a normal social schedule for at least a small portion of the week. But the fact remains that they are the least healthy option because they involve repeatedly uprooting the circadian clock.

When melatonin levels decrease, some tumours grow much faster, which is thought to account for the increased risk to these workers, whose melatonin levels never quite synchronize with their sleep-wake schedules. A slowly rotating morning-afternoon-evening shift schedule is easier for the body to accommodate than evening-afternoon-morning, just as travelling west—extending a day instead of contracting it—is less of a strain than heading east. On a fast rotation in either direction, adaptation is hopeless and performance suffers, but swing shifters have the advantage of catching up on sleep after day shifts.

Day and night waking shifts in human society have historically been indicators of socio-economic class. Many of the dirtiest jobs have been done under cover of darkness, and the night shift has been the realm of the underclass, the criminal sector and a cast of untouchables. Night soil removers carted away human waste while its creators slept, and to this day, garbage collectors often work in the very early morning, before the smell-sensitive public deign to put their noses outside. Even the air at night was seen as unhealthy in medieval England, and shutters were closed to keep it out for fear of disease. Prostitutes ("ladies of the night") ply their trade, through varying degrees of legality, after dark, and thieves or the highwaymen of the past use night's anonymity to hide their misdeeds.

From bouncers to factory workers, shifts that remove people from daytime communal life also keep them from the ranks of power. It is a privilege to work during the throng of business hours and then retire to private life, leaving garbage on the curb for the invisible class to remove. Sleeping during the night, the upper socio-economic classes literally close their eyes to the struggles of the toiling poor.

When I interviewed chronobiologist Jim Waterhouse, he speculated that if, over an evolutionary time scale, a group of nocturnal humans emerged, they might be so temporally separated from
the rest of us that they would form a new species. As wild and
improbable as we both know this is, it shows how biology makes
use of all four dimensions of space and time, and separation in
time is just as powerful as geographic separation to keep two
waking humans apart. It's no wonder marriages between larks
and night owls lead to survey reports of more arguments and less
satisfaction in general. Incompatible chronotypes should perhaps
be added to the relationship warning signs in women's magazine
quizzes. Still, some couples make it work, with each even using
the other's schedule to moderate his or her own schedule toward
the mean, or finding quiet time in the "uninhabited" hours.

History is scattered with disasters stemming from human errors on
the night shift. Whether because of fatigue, circadian mental low
points or organizational factors like lower-seniority night shifters in positions of responsibility, the wee hours are a dangerous
time for judgment calls involving safety. On December 3, 1984, in
Bhopal, India, night workers at a Union Carbide pesticide plant
were cleaning out the pipes connected to three tanks of methyl
isocyanate. Whether accidentally or by sabotage (as the company
maintains), hundreds of gallons of water were pumped into one
tank, triggering an exothermic chemical reaction that raised the
internal temperature over 200 degrees Celsius. A refrigeration
system that might have prevented this had been shut down five
months earlier. When thousands of pounds of the deadly gas were
vented, a flare tower designed to burn off the gas was not operating, and the densely residential surrounding area was exposed,
suffocating thousands before an evacuation could be ordered.

Clearly the failing safety systems should have made the plant inoperable, but the conditions of night work there were found to be a contributing factor; for example, there was no maintenance supervisor on the night shift. When a skeleton crew heads up an operation in the interlude between fully staffed day shifts, pared-down oversight is not unusual.

Fatigue had a hand in the space shuttle *Challenger* disaster soon thereafter. After a night full of troubleshooting that left room for less than two hours of sleep, the NASA managers made the decision to launch despite warnings from engineers that the sub-zero weather could cause a failure. The O-rings sealing the solid rocket booster joints had not been thoroughly tested at low temperatures, and the engineers argued they might not seal properly. Indeed, they failed to seal, precipitating the disintegration of the shuttle and the deaths of all aboard it.

If a night of sleep deprivation can cloud the judgment of spacecraft professionals ramped up for the event of their careers—paying close attention, in other words—imagine having a life-and-death decision of your own made by a medical intern at the close of a thirty-hour shift. As intuitively dangerous as this seems, marathon shifts are integral to the training regimen at many hospitals, on the premise that the more patients a doctor sees, the better equipped he or she will be to rise through the ranks. While other industries set far shorter limits on work hours, medicine makes an exception. The result is a diagnosis by someone who could be legally drunk, given his or her level of cognitive impairment. These interns are a danger to themselves as well, having a much higher risk of stabbing themselves with a needle or scalpel. Then they drive home.

Apart from experiencing levels of fatigue that are functionally equivalent to alcohol intoxication, night shifters are more likely to have drug and alcohol abuse problems that likely affect their performance. They have higher divorce rates because of disruptions to the couple's joint social life and poor contact with children, and they suffer more accidents driving to and from work. Gastrointestinal problems and infertility increase, as do mood swings. As a result, 20 percent of shift workers drop out in their first year and 33 percent in their second, because of health concerns.

There seems to be a social night shift as well as a professional one—countercultures often adopt nocturnal lifestyles, either to thrive under cover of darkness or simply to have the place to themselves while the mainstream masses are asleep. As Ray Ray in the 1992 film *South Central* declares, "You can't control the day: the Man controls the day. But we will control the night."

One such reaction against the tyranny of the diurnal mainstream is the phenomenon that has turned many Japanese youth into *hikikomori*. The term roughly translates into "people who withdraw," and refers to thousands of societal dropouts who refuse to come out of their bedrooms for an extended period (loosely defined by a six-month stint or longer). Oppressed by insanely high academic expectations and a pass-or-fail notion of success, students can sometimes give up entirely following a failure they see as derailing their future. Instead of heading out for cram school, they sleep during the day and enjoy limited social contact through online gaming at night. The less socially phobic might emerge into the darkness to pick up junk food at the local twenty-four-hour convenience store. Since most Japanese people live at home until they're married, *hikikomori* are still close to their families and are fed and cared for during their isolation. The strain on the rest of the family is immense.

The evidence is mostly anecdotal. It's hard to collect statistics on people who won't leave their rooms to answer a survey. The anecdotes have piled up, however, and now qualify as a phenomenon.

One psychiatrist drew attention to the problem by estimating the numbers of *hikikomori* at more than a million—20 percent of the typical *hikikomori* demographic of male adolescents in Japan. The estimate's objectivity was later undermined when it emerged that he had based it on the prevalence of schizophrenia (1 per cent of the overall population) because he felt he saw just as many *hikikomori* in his practice as schizophrenics.

A kidnapping and a murder helped push the Japanese phenomenon into the spotlight. In January 2002, a nineteen-year-old woman was rescued after being held captive for ten years by a thirty-seven-year-old man. And in May of that year, a seventeen-year-old hijacked a bus and killed one of the passengers. Both of the men responsible were described as *hikikomori*. But whenever these types of stories catch on in the Western media, as these did in *Time* magazine and on the BBC, among other sources, we need to exercise some skepticism.

Most of the stories have started off the same way: "Takeshi used to be a normal kid. He liked video games and soccer. Now his family lives under a *shroud of terror*. Takeshi hasn't come out of his bedroom in three years except to scream at his mother and send her out for more video games." There has been a persistent tendency in the coverage to link the phenomenon to violent behaviour. One article is called "Hikikomori: Homicidal Teens of Japan." Another, "Natural Born Killers?" And another, "Japan's Teen Hermits Spread Fear." How can a hermit spread anything?

What's frustrating about these articles is not just that they sensationalize the real problems of people who just want to be left alone, but that they continue to perpetuate ideas about Japan based on simplistic stereotypes. Every time the Western media finds out about some new social phenomena in Japan, it's the same thing: horrifying anecdotal evidence followed by pop psychology that invokes images of feudal Japan. In the 1980s it was *karoshi*—death from overwork—frenzied workers' hearts exploding while they sat at their desks, the honourable Japanese devotion to the company forcing people to sacrifice their lives, like so many samurai committing hara-kiri before their lords.

Typical behaviour is described here by BBC reporter Phil Rees: "Traditional Japan valued the nobility of solitude. Samurai warriors trained in isolation rather than be seen as imperfect ... Increasing numbers of young people feel they can't fit in; more and more are seeking the sanctuary of solitude." If you were to look back at all the practices traditional Europe valued—duelling at dawn or monks wearing hair shirts, for example—you could make all kinds of inferences about the admittedly strange behaviour of European teenagers too, but I'm not sure it would get to the heart of the matter.

Japan's suicide rate is twice Canada's. Government corruption is universal. They're still using a constitution written in English by General MacArthur's undersecretaries. Statistics from the Ministry of Education, Culture, Sports, Science and Technology show that the number of children refusing to attend school has doubled in the past ten years. Rather than do the long, hard work of researching the social history of Japan, Western journalists often fall back on one-dimensional analogies of samurai and geishas. Angst, depression and withdrawal are the hallmarks of teenagers worldwide. Granted, they've taken it to the next level in Japan. But while Japanese psychiatrists search for a program or a cure, Mitsunori Iwata, who recovered from a seven-year period of being a *hikikomori*, explains that his recovery came about from nurturing and encouragement from people who believed in him, a groundbreaking innovation that may even have applications in the West.

✿

If manipulating circadian rhythms is controversial, preventing them from manipulating you—fighting jet lag, for instance—is less so. People have a wide range of responses to the mismatch between inside and outside time. Apart from the effects of the fatiguing rigours of a long journey, which wear off in a day, global travel can put you off your game for a week or more. In combatting the worst of it, the principle to keep in mind is this: Body clocks are biased toward resetting to a later time because they naturally cycle with a period longer than twenty-four hours. This means when you fly west with the sun, your circadian rhythms catch up more quickly than when you fly east against the sun, and if the time difference is more than ten hours, you're best to adjust by changing to a later and later schedule, through the clock, rather than advancing. Expert advice is mainly based on the idea of strengthening your destination's time cues from the start—preferably before you even fly, shifting your day's routine of sleep and mealtimes to match more closely the rhythm they'll have at your destination. It's only really an issue if you're crossing four time zones or more, unless you end up sleeping on the plane during daytime (don't).

For a trip of less than four days, forget about really adjusting to the new time zone. Just schedule important meetings for hours when your internal clock is set to daytime, assuming you have control over your schedule. Longer trips involve staying as strict with yourself as humanly possible—not sleeping in more than a couple of hours, eating meals on local time whether you feel like

JET-LAG TOOL KIT
- British Airways online jet lag calculator
- Virgin Atlantic Jet Lag Fighter for iPhone and iPad
- Melatonin supplements to be taken before sleep
- Sunglasses to limit blue-light exposure at certain times of day; it can reset your body clock in the wrong direction
- Sleeping mask
- Running shoes for exercising at the prescribed time of day

it or not, and keeping your eyelids open any way you can until bedtime. A day or two beforehand, shift your sleeping schedule by an hour or two for an extra edge. On the plane, try living as though you're at your destination already, resetting your watch right away and sleeping only if it's night where you're going. The meal schedule on the plane won't always cooperate, but it's worth getting a jump on your adjustment. When it comes to plane food, unless you're famished you can't go too wrong with fasting. Eating when your body thinks it's nighttime will lead to indigestion (likely exacerbated by poor-quality plane food). You may be dead tired when you arrive, simply from getting up early and lugging baggage around all day, so nap if you must, but make it brief.

The body clock can shift by one or two time zones per day going east and two or three per day travelling west. Bright light is the crucial cue, as always, and it's important to be active outdoors in the daytime. But there's one important caveat, which requires a certain amount of calculation: Bright light in the early morning (according to your body clock) will advance your clock, making you wake up earlier the next morning. In the late evening, subjectively, it will delay your clock. So sometimes, even when it's daytime and sunny outside at your travel destination, you'll want to stay indoors to avoid setting back your adjustment efforts. Often a jet-lag sufferer will wake up long before the alarm clock calls. In these situations, stay in bed quietly until the appointed rising time. Taking melatonin before bed (if it's available in your country) is generally understood to help you acclimatize, but research on this particular substance is limited by the fact that it's native to our bodies and thus can't be patented. Big Pharma has no interest in exploring its effects because there's no profit to be made from it.

The ultimate jet lag happens when our environment is so totally different from the norm that daily light cues are not merely absent, but perhaps actively conflict with our behavioural cycles. Four crew members of the 1991 space shuttle *Columbia* were faced with a daunting challenge: a launch scheduled for one o'clock in the morning. Harvard sleep expert Dr. Charles Czeisler realigned the crew's internal clocks over the course of three quarantine days. By launch day, the astronauts were nocturnal animals.

I've always just kind of winged it (no pun intended) when it comes to jet lag, often surprised by the suddenness and seeming randomness of its effects and their timing. Knowing the advice of the experts now I decide to test it out. An invitation to TED provides the excuse. TED—short for Technology, Entertainment, Design—is an ideas conference that has grown beyond all the physical boundaries of an auditorium to become something of an open university. Speakers have exactly eighteen minutes to convey a new idea in language accessible to the educated layman, and the TED website is packed full of the most important living thinkers in the world. A team of three thousand-odd translators makes the lectures available in seventy-seven languages. When I was invited to give a short talk at TED Global in Oxford, I was both thrilled and intimidated as I imagined speaking to a roomful of the movers and shakers I've watched in their online talks. The event lasts for a week and, wanting to get the full experience there without leaving my family for too long, I set about planning my jet-lag strategy.

There are eight time zones between Yellowknife and Oxford. Eight hours of body clock confusion amid a packed schedule of lectures, library tours and cocktails. I need a game plan to make sure I don't sleep through the best parts and end up pacing back and forth in a hotel room at four in the morning. Enter the wealth of computerized hand-held devices and smart phones this decade has delivered. Not only can you be notified before every appointment and intentionally woken up by a telephone, but mobile technology now includes programs that will hold an international traveller's hand through the perils of jet lag. A quick search of the application store on my iPhone reveals the Virgin Atlantic Jet Lag Fighter.

I enter my demographic details into the program as well as my regular sleep and natural waking times, presumably to give it an idea of my chronotype: lark or owl. Then it asks for my takeoff and landing times for both my departure and return trips. Though it will guide me through shifting my sleep times before my trip, it warns me that this is difficult to implement and that manipulating light exposure once I get to England will be much more effective in cutting my adjustment time in half. It even reminds me that sleep hormone supplements like melatonin are available over the counter where I live, but not in Europe, so I should stock up before I leave if I intend to use some gentle sleep drugs.

In the three days before my overnight flight from Yellowknife to Calgary to Heathrow, I'm instructed to get up and go to bed an hour earlier each day, culminating in a seven thirty bedtime on the eve of my flight and a five-in-the-morning start on the day of. It seems counterintuitive with such a long day ahead of me—a red-eye flight that's exhausting at the best of times—to be up and packing at the crack of dawn, but I plug along to the best of my ability. I draw the line at missing my son's bedtime rituals on the last night, though, so seven thirty becomes eight thirty after bath time and story time.

I rehearse my TED talk on the plane, clicking through PowerPoint slides until the cabin dims. I'm meant to avoid light in the late morning, which is only partly possible since I'm negotiating Heathrow for half of it and then waiting outdoors for a bus to Oxford. Then I'm prescribed a two-hour dose of natural light in the early afternoon, which I take in through the bus windows. Stepping off the bus, all I want to do is collapse in front of a television with a giant bottle of water, but the Jet Lag Fighter is still fighting, telling me to exercise for an hour between five thirty and six thirty in the evening. It's a good excuse to check out the university gardens, so I lace up my running shoes and bounce my discombobulated self through greener grass than I've seen all year in the Subarctic.

There's a graph on the screen that tells me the unfortunate cretins who haven't taken a sleep program are already two hours behind me in their sleep adjustment. At the same time, my iPhone warns me I'm not at my best and shouldn't entrust myself with monotonous activities that could endanger others. Two days into the conference, I'm on Greenwich Mean Time, body and soul, whereas the Jet Lag Fighter assures me I'd have taken the whole week to adjust otherwise—just in time to fly back to Yellowknife and start the process again.

Not only are many of the conference attendees aware of Jet Lag Fighter but they also swear by an even more popular app called Sleep Cycle alarm clock, out of Maciek Drejak Labs. I download it to give it a shot and I'm floored by its simple ingenuity. Using the iPhone's accelerometer, the program monitors my movements overnight to determine what stage of sleep I'm in at any given time. It stands to reason that when you wake up, the longer you have slept, the better you should feel. But anyone who's taken a three-hour nap can tell you that a longer sleep can sometimes leave you groggier than a short one. Just as important as the duration of sleep is the phase of sleep you're in at the moment when you wake up. If an alarm sounds and drags you from the deepest point of your cycle, you may hit the snooze button and retreat to dream-land before you even register that it's morning—if, indeed, you hear the alarm at all.

I set the phone to *airplane mode* to cut the radiation before I place it under the sheets at the head of my bed—otherwise thoughts of my constantly irradiated brain would presumably give me insomnia and spoil the experiment. I set my alarm for six thirty in the hopes of springing out of bed in time to go for an organized run with the fittest of my TED compatriots. But six thirty isn't really a magic time, it's just a time when I'd like to awake. The alarm will sound sometime between six and six thirty at a moment when my sleep cycle is at its lightest phase. Any sleep lost by earlier waking is more than compensated by the ease of waking. The next morning, Sleep Cycle chirps at me, and though it takes a minute to untangle the phone from the bed, I'm poring voyeuristically over the graph it created of my sleeping patterns— when I was dreaming, when I was in deep sleep, the time I got up and went to the bathroom—before I realize how normal I feel despite the ungodly hour. Mission accomplished.

TEN

spreading our western ways

The yellow tent was a big mistake on my part. I've packed it in early, having braved a long day of air travel to get to Inuvik, Northwest Territories, and I've been looking forward to resting my bones on my spiffy new goose-down sleeping mat. I never sleep as well as I do when I'm camping.

But two hours after I zip up the tent flap, a searing canary-yellow light is burning through my eyelids. It's eleven at night, by my watch, but the July sun is still out in full force, and there's little chance of sleep for me. Luckily, my fatigue seems to have dissipated since my arrival anyway. I sit up and hear a giggle.

A little girl is peering in the vestibule of my tent, checking out the stranger camping on a lawn in town. She can't be more than nine, but through the yellow fly opening I see younger children still, circling a bare patch of land on their bikes. A log and a couple of two-by-fours are set up as a makeshift ramp to entertain the braver of the cyclists.

"Hi there," I say to the girl, surprised my voice isn't groggy from my nap.

She smiles shyly and trots off to join her friends.

When I was her age, my bedtime was eight o'clock. I had to be in my pajamas well before that, and it was a rare day that I stepped outside the house after our six-thirty dinner. But these kids are just getting started at eleven o'clock *at night*. What's more, they seem quite happy to run their own show—there isn't an adult in sight to supervise them.

I put on my shoes and go for a wander. My hosts run the outfit that will be taking me canoeing down a tundra river the following morning. Their passion is dogsledding, and in the summertime they subsidize their kennels with ecotourism dollars, organizing logistics for remote, northern, wilderness adventures.

My tent is set up in a far corner of their lot, and judging from the incessant barking, the kennels are on the far side of their house. I can't even count the dogs. Every few metres, there's a metal post in the ground with a chain attached. A dog circles at its perimeter. To the side, chicken-wire cages house the puppies with their mothers.

Two jet-black ravens, emblematic tricksters of the northern bird world, are teasing one of the dogs, who's gnawing on a bone. Another raven struts provocatively within range of the dog's chain, invading his small territory. When the sled dog leaps up to snap at the raven, the bird's companion swoops in to snatch his dropped bone.

They're all huskies, but they don't have the furry white bulk I associate with the breed. These guys are scrawny, and they don't look strong enough to run the Iditarod or the Yukon Quest. Still, I know their owners are up there with the best mushers in the world, so the dogs' looks must be deceiving.

I'll admit that I have a mild fear of dogs—mostly just of the kind that jump up or bark. It's the unpredictability of their movements that gets me, and I often wonder if I have some kind of hypersensitive startle response. This pack is about as unruly a bunch as I've seen, and they're clearly not treated as pets. I wouldn't call their conditions cruel or inhumane in any way, but it's clear that these are working dogs, yet to be softened through social interaction with humans.

They certainly lack the guide-dog calm that puts me at ease, and something has them riled up to a frenzy. Luckily for me, the source of their excitement is on the opposite side of the kennels, and he has a bucket of food and a shovel.

Boogie Pokiak is an Inuvialuit elder who comes into Inuvik for the odd stint of summer work. His weathered skin, worn teeth and greying hair stand in stark contrast to his obvious physical strength and vitality. Now, he's taking care of the kennels in a season when the dogs get to recuperate from their hard winter's work. Pokiak invites me to help him exercise the dogs. They don't seem like the kind that would heel at the end of a leash, but that's not what he has in mind.

Next to the house, a four-wheeler idles with a multi-branched harness hooked to its front end. Pokiak chooses a dog to detach from its pole and drags it by the collar to the waiting vehicle. "This girl's the leader," he says, as he attaches her to the longest rope. One by one he marshals four more dogs and hooks them up. As soon as they're released from his grip, the dogs strain at their harnesses. It's as if they have been waiting to pull something all along—they clearly love their work. Good thing the four-wheeler's emergency brake is on.

Pokiak makes a quick phone call in Inuvialuktun, the local tongue that's hardly spoken at all anymore by the younger generations. Then we hop onto the four-wheeler and he releases the handbrake. The dogs know where they're going and they waste no time in pulling away from the kennels onto the main, circular

Inuvik road. Snow or no snow, they were bred to pull in teams, and this is what they live for.

The leader is trailed by two pairs of dogs, and the pair closest to me and Pokiak seem a little less disciplined. The dog on the left snaps playfully at the other every once in a while, and his friend on the right is easily distracted by children or ravens on the side of the road. "This is the first year for those two," explains Pokiak. "We're starting to train them up this summer. They'll get the idea soon enough."

Nearing the main drag, we pass some government offices. The territorial bureaucracy stations its health department and Western Arctic administration here. The buildings are the swankest in town, but they've been closed for a good six hours now. Despite the constant feeling of daytime, the offices work on the same nine-to-five schedule, summer or winter, dovetailing nicely with the federal government offices in the south.

What the office buildings lack in life, however, the bars make up for in bustling activity. We ride past the Mad Trapper Pub, where karaoke night is in full swing, with every generation of the town well represented. No one bats an eye as our dog team thunders by with us in tow. Teenagers in the latest hip-hop gear play pool in the front room. Most of them are working for the oil companies, manning the sounding trucks that rumble along straight, cleared roads in the wilderness, measuring echoes for signs of underground riches. The money's so good for a sixteen-year-old it's hard to keep them from dropping out of the local subpar high school.

It seems like Pokiak could run these dogs in his sleep, so I start asking him about himself. He's from the Inuvialuit hamlet of Tuktoyaktuk—known locally as Tuk—which received recent worldwide attention during a hit television series called *Ice Road Truckers*. The History Channel documentary team followed truck drivers as they navigated the winter road from Inuvik to Tuk, bringing oil- and gas-industry supplies through the resource-rich

Mackenzie delta while the Mackenzie River was frozen thick enough for trucks to cross.

For Pokiak, the series was just the latest of several strange incursions into his community, many of which have brought prosperity to Tuk. Boogie and his brother James run one of the last polar-bear hunting outfits in Canada. American hunters pay big bucks for the chance to bag a polar bear for the Super Slam of North American Big Game—in which each member attempts to achieve a twenty-nine-animal collection that could fill a trophy room. The local hunter and trapper association has a set number of hunting tags to use on polar bears each year. When hunters make the kill, they have to celebrate abstemiously. A dry community, Tuk keeps social problems in check by asking visitors not to bring alcohol into the area.

I point out the children, still screaming around in packs on their little bikes. "Summer," he says, as if that explains it all. This is the way it's always been here. Summer is a time of almost manic hunting and working. The sun is ever-present in the sky, and it's enough to fool the body into relinquishing much of its need for sleep. All the sluggishness, lethargy and depression that can accompany a High Arctic winter are reversed in summer, leading to elevated mood, energy and drive. There have even been cases of a kind of pathological seasonal mania during northern summers—the flip side of winter blues.

Pokiak says the Inuvialuit traditional way of life has been better preserved in the summer and fall, when many hunters still venture into the wild to harvest caribou and live there for weeks on end. The community has been more affected by modernization during the wintertime, which was traditionally reserved for staying warm inside and enjoying the company of the family. In a kind of semi-hibernation, the Inuvialuit lived off stored meat from summer hunts and dozed through much of the winter.

Now they're expected to maintain their businesses through a full working day, even when their bodies protest under the soporific darkness. Inuvik's government workers trudge wearily through their paper-filled days, heads nodding toward their desks. Snowmobiles roar through Arctic towns, headlights flickering beneath waving green aurora borealis.

We round the bend into the kennels again, and I thank Pokiak and excuse myself, knowing I've got an early start in the morning. It's starting to feel like evening now, and I think I could nod off after winding down with a little reading in my tent. I stop to tie my shoe by the house, and there's a strange shift in perspective. When I rise, I feel a rush of energy, like it's no longer evening— now it's mid-morning all of a sudden and the day holds the promise of adventure and achievement.

Clearly my body's confused. I check my watch. Sure enough, it's around midnight. The sun has reached the lowest point in the sky and, as of a moment ago, it's beginning to rise again. I slip back into my bright yellow tent, pick up my book and sigh. So much for sleep.

Inuvik's government and business operating hours are in stark contrast to the local climatic rhythms. There is still a feeling of constant day in Inuvik's summer life.

Wherever I travel, I find these glaring discrepancies at the junctures of two cultures. Like any other cultural attribute— food, ideas, the people themselves—our circadian rhythms travel as part of a package, and daily habits are spread along trading routes. This might be called *circadian imperialism*. The particular custom that's been imported to Inuvik—the nine-to-five year-round work schedule—has a long history and is perhaps the most common introductory phase instilled by circadian imperialism. In developing countries, of course, the introduced working day is much longer, but still impervious to environmentally and socially relevant rhythms.

Recent arrivals to the poles—the regions most drastically affected by changing seasons—have brought with them the year-round nine-to-five schedule. The Amundsen-Scott South Pole

Station in Antarctica and the Eureka High Arctic Weather Station on Ellesmere Island follow strict, uniform timetables no matter where the sun is. Given the health hazards of stress, circadian dysfunction, overwork and interference with proper digestion, we must accept that some short-term profit trade-offs must be made for the sake of long-term—which is to say, lifelong—productivity.

It's still worse for those employed in the resource-based econ-omy: Diamond mines run a two-weeks-in, two-weeks-out shift model. Workers fly up to "camp" where they labour underground to tap out the kimberlite pipes or run machinery in the diamond-processing plants. The camp's social life is quite regimented, with no alcohol permitted on-site and a close watch kept for drugs. Anyone with access to raw or finished diamonds is subject to

ATTEN-*TION*!

Basic military training is looked upon with dread by new recruits hoping for a career in the U.S. military. They hope only to survive the initiation without breaking. But a look at the performance standards tells quite a lenient story. Though there are variations according to branch and local-ity, the U.S. military requires a minute or two of push-ups (not more than fifty for men and less than half that for women), similar intensity for sit-ups and a timed run of two miles. None of the activities during the three months or so of basic training are beyond the capabilities of a reasonably fit seventeen- to twenty-one-year-old.

A look at the daily schedule, however, reveals why it all may seem so tough. Trainees are rudely awakened at 4:30 A.M. and subjected to the hardest exercise during the early mornings—the least optimal circadian time for physical performance—which leads to feelings of exhaustion. Though lights-out times allow for a reasonable amount of sleep, the early start puts new recruits into an artificial jet lag. It helps create the stress that will eventually lead a soldier to break down his ego to place duty ahead of self.

various searches for the sake of security. Then, in their two weeks out, workers are left to their own devices. Often the jarring disconnect between a structured work life and two weeks of aimless rest can feed addiction cycles and binging. Parents who return after not seeing their children for half of the month feel at the same time neglectful and unneeded. Community life has gone on without them, and they in turn feel less connection to what, culturally, would have been tight-knit extended family group-ings. Meanwhile, the higher-ranking specialists at the mines—the human resources professionals, the computer technicians, etc.—are afforded more frequent flights in and out. They work on a four-days-in, four-days-out routine that approximates a lax workweek followed by a long weekend.

Modern customs, many of them associated with changes brought about by the Industrial Revolution, are taking precedence over the daily rhythms prescribed by local cultures around the world. Discussions surrounding these issues tend to be tinged with racist nonsense about work ethic and discipline, but the reality is that these places had schedules that made sense before, and they are dealing with an incongruous imposition of alien schedules as best they can.

Even as we try to understand other cultures, we have a simultan-eous and opposing societal drive to keep them at arm's length and to judge them by our own culture's standards. Ultimately, we try to change them, as we do every other aspect of our environment, with the conquering mindset that pervades Western history.

Other cultures' daily customs and biological responses to local conditions can come into conflict with the demands of the marketplace. In the modern always-on day, they've had to adjust and adapt, whether or not it makes for a comfortable living situation. The Toshiba engineer in Japan's productivity-oriented culture may spend a week working twenty-hour days at the office, and then sleep through all of Sunday, rising only for refreshment. The "salaryman" system there entails a lifelong job at a single company, where all waking hours are spent with colleagues, even while engaged in leisure pursuits. Often a new father will be transferred away from his hometown, so that parenting activities do not interfere with productivity, with troubling results for both children and fathers. Since the country's economic crisis, starting in the 1990s, this system of lifelong employment, with its emphasis on seniority, is gradually ceding to a meritocracy with more labour mobility. But the pressure to succeed for the good of your family is stronger than ever, beginning in childhood and never really letting up.

Once we get past the need to refuel every few hours, our eating patterns become more socially governed than matters of physical necessity. In many countries, the day's structure is enshrined in custom or labour law—mandatory morning coffee breaks and afternoon tea breaks, as well as a lunch break. A multi-billion-dollar coffee-shop industry has sprung up around these entrenched rhythms. After work, employees in most Western countries sit down for a large meal. Dr. Jim Waterhouse is an expert on circadian rhythms and metabolism. I reach him at his home in Liverpool, England. "We do not need to eat nearly as frequently as we do. You can see it in the obesity levels around the Western world," says Waterhouse. "The social functions of eating and drinking have taken over." Family get-togethers focused on eating are followed by working breakfasts and dinner dates. We meet friends for coffee or drinks or smoothies.

"Within a given culture, one sees individual differences based on preference—people who skip breakfast or eat light dinners compared to their lunches," says Waterhouse. When the body's fluids become too concentrated, we are thirsty. Hunger is related to falling glucose levels, but the amount we eat in a given meal is virtually unrelated to how hungry we were before it. "Most of the people we've studied eat slightly less during the week than they would need to maintain their body weight," says Waterhouse. "Then they make up for it on the weekend, when they splurge on brunches or social dinners with alcohol." Basically, the daily timing of meals doesn't seem to have much connection to underlying circadian rhythms—this, despite our feeling that it's dinnertime, which turns out to be mostly a matter of habit. One habit carries a particularly strong illusion of being intrinsically rhythmic: the urge to defecate. "Most people go to the toilet once a day. It's provoked by eating, when the stomach's fullness triggers a reflex," says Waterhouse. "Our sensation of that reflex is strongest after fasting, so most people defecate after having breakfast. We haven't found a body clock link yet."

That's not to say that the body doesn't link its metabolizing of all that food to its circadian system. Insulin released from the pancreas and blood sugar are strongly connected to time of day. Waterhouse conducted a study to test circadian effects on weight loss. "We had our subjects eat a meal either at breakfast time or at dinner time. The ones who ate it in the morning lost weight, but the others didn't," recalls Waterhouse. That's because our bodies deal best with food in the daytime and use our fat for overnight energy.

Human circadian circuitry gets really interesting when you consider all the systems that have daily rhythms. Cardiac, muscular, intestinal and hormonal systems all follow a dance through the day. There is some order in the chaos, though—a lot of it boils down to body temperature.

Recording body temperature over the course of a few months also provides an illustration of the menstrual cycle's effect. Premenstrual syndrome, a pattern of physical and emotional symptoms that peaks late in a woman's menstrual cycle, is a circadian malfunction: During the second half of the menstrual cycle, some women's circadian rhythms accelerate. This causes more melatonin to be released, which cuts off supplies of the neurotransmitters serotonin and progesterone, which in turn leads to pain, irritability and insomnia. It turns out that bright light is an effective therapy for premenstrual syndrome, because it dampens melatonin levels while resetting circadian pace.

There's a big difference between the environment in bed with the lights off and that of an active day outside, so it can be tricky to tease out natural cycles that exist underneath the effects of behaviour. Researchers have their subjects try all manner of different schedules around the clock to see what stays constant. They find that blood pressure and body temperature rise and fall predictably over the course of the day, even in someone lying quietly and watching television for twenty-four hours. At its lowest just before dawn, core temperature rises gradually to peak in the early evening, and drops sharply before sleep. It seems to me that if you know your body well enough, you can apply that knowledge to countless decisions. Catch lung function at its peak between four and six in the evening, and you might set a new personal running record, for example. If you've ever felt drowsy after a hot bath, you likely raised your body temperature while bathing. The sharp return to normal when you got out to dry off simulates the evening body cooling before bed, and your brain is fooled into a rapid preparation for sleep.

Artificial light—fires fed by wood, peat or coal, or lanterns fuelled by whale oil or paraffin—changed everything. People who formerly were chained to the unalterable cycle of daylight and nighttime darkness were set free. Electricity has taken this liberation to new heights, to the point where our lives are lived in a perpetual mid-afternoon in May. In the same way that we, as a species, have plumbed the depths of the oceans—a place our bodies were never built to explore—and populated the polar regions using heating technologies fuelled by sources ranging from whale oil to electricity, humans have also been pioneering a new world in the fourth dimension, conquering hours, rather than space. We have colonized the night.

Instead of the spacesuit for moonwalks on distant orbiting spheres, we suit up in our technology—our cars, our flashlights, our trains—surrounded in balls of light, to take us into the oceans of darkness we were never built to roam in. In the earliest days, torches led the way into that void; then, five thousand years ago agriculture gave us vegetable oil, a much cheaper fuel for lamps. Paris pioneered the coordinated use of street lighting in the late 1600s, followed a hundred years later by London.

But society still has to deal with the reality that most of the world, the part we don't create around us, gets dark at night.

Darkness comes gradually, in stages. The United States Naval Observatory has defined three phases of dusk: *civil twilight, nautical twilight and astronomical twilight.* Just after the sun sets and colours take on the surreal saturations that create what photographers call the magic hour, civil twilight sets in. Though it might not seem like visibility is impaired, this is when car headlights should be flicked on. Half an hour later comes nautical twilight, when the North Star in the northern hemisphere and the Southern

Cross on the other side of the world become visible for navigating. Finally, astronomical twilight arrives after another hour or so. The weakest light from distant stars makes it through the "noise" of the atmosphere and, provided you're away from the city, the telescopes come out. In winter, this might happen by eight o'clock.

Meanwhile, in the domestic sphere, eight o'clock traditionally marks the children's hour, made famous by Longfellow's poem of the same name. The poem describes him in his study, watching his three young daughters come tripping down the stairs to visit him at the appointed hour. There is such joy in the poem, such glee at the anticipation of seeing his children—reading it evokes in me a bittersweet feeling. I'm reminded of how recently fathers were not encouraged to be involved in their young children's upbringing, even though they might have the greatest aptitude and calling for it.

Now, of course, eight o'clock is prime time in the television world and typically bedtime for children. This serves the dual purposes of allowing naturally larkish children the sleep they need for optimal development and of giving their parents a couple of hours of leisure in the late evening. Eight o'clock is now a typical bedtime for children ages six through ten. Interestingly, bedtimes have, on average, been creeping later by half an hour each decade. I'd like to know whether this is accounted for by an increasing number of families who don't institute bedtimes at all. That is, whether the culture has reverted to a less rule-based family environment, concurrent with less of a hierarchical divide between parent and child. If this is the case, many children may simply be staying up and watching the same television programs as their parents and drifting off when they're too exhausted to keep their eyes open or being sent to bed when they're too cranky to comfortably tolerate.

Even television programming itself may not only reflect its audience's daily rhythms but also form them. Certain days of the week might entail staying up later than usual or rescheduling dinner just to catch the latest instalment of *Jersey Shore* or *Monday Night Football.*

　　　　　　　　　　　🕭

All humans have the same circadian rhythms, but our unique intelligence has led us to accommodate the cycle in very different ways throughout history. We know that people whose lives have been governed by the natural cycle of day and night, without the disruptions created by artificial light and modern technology, have very different sleep patterns from those most of us follow now. Similarly, pre-industrial society had profoundly different birthing patterns, in keeping with the rhythms of their lives. While North Americans can spend most of their time oblivious to the weather outside, pre-industrial agricultural societies felt the climate in their homes and on their plates. They also had to time their births to coincide with nature's bounty and the logistics of pregnancy and neonatal care, whether through cultural practices or seasonal variability in fertility.

Animals outside of the equatorial zones usually have a mating season and a birthing or hatching season. The rest of the year they conserve energy, with the males regressing their gonads and both sexes focusing on survival. Humans, in contrast, have always been able—strictly in biological terms—to conceive and give birth all year round. When a population's birth data are compiled, however, patterns emerge—and those patterns are much stronger in the absence of artificial light and season-less, thermostat-driven temperature control.

In the far North, conception peaks in summer when the temperature is mildest. Around the equator it peaks during the few months of cool relief. Everywhere in between, where climate encompasses a range of temperatures, conception is at its highest when morning minimum temperatures hit 12 degrees Celsius. As with plant flowering, the closer a population is to the equator, the earlier in the year the temperature hits that mark and the earlier conception peaks. That translates into two bumps in North American births—one in April and another in November. In the southern hemisphere, of course, the peaks are offset by six months.

Our agrarian ancestors likely conceived after harvest time, when good nutrition primed ovarian function. The Lese women of Congo experience drops in estrogen and progesterone as a result of weight loss before the harvest, and menstruation slows or halts. This may explain why the hunter-gatherer societies that have survived have a gendered division of labour. Hunters—almost exclusively male—travel vast distances every day. As with female athletes today, this energy burden on females who tried hunting would have led to amenorrhea (suspension of periods). The resulting vanishing birth rate in the population of female hunters would have been followed by the disappearance of that society.

Sometimes culture dictates the seasons for conception, often reinforcing the very pattern that biology promotes. Papua New Guinea's Samukundi harvest their crops in January. According to their belief system, from July until harvest time—fully half the year—sex is prohibited; consequently, births peak strongly in October. A more subtle effect was found in Inuit who socialized with the broader community during winter, and then retreated to hunting and fishing camps with their immediate families during summer. Conception peaked in the privacy of their summer camps and births followed in the first half of the calendar year.

A spring-birth peak still occurs in modern times, but the effect is much weaker. Spain under Franco in the 1960s offers a dramatic example: When the Spanish moved en masse to industrialized, indoor jobs, their annual birth rhythm—formerly very obvious in March and April—collapsed into a much more even distribution over the months.

Occasionally, we speculate as to what might be happening if only our lifestyles were not so cozy. In November 1965, the electricity failed across 207,000 square kilometres of northeastern United States and Canada. More than 30 million people lost power for roughly a day. The *New York Times* interviewed doctors the following August, who reported noticing a mini baby boom, suggesting that one day of forced family time had been equivalent to an unplanned couples' retreat, but a subsequent statistical study by demographer J. Richard Udry debunked the theory.

Four months have passed since my arrival in Japan. I have established a comfortable life for myself, teaching English and attending the university in Kyoto. Compared with the naive young woman who first stepped into the tiny Kyoto apartment, I am almost unrecognizable. Extended culture shock and gruelling adaptation have taken their toll, and I am pasty and unfit, bleary and groggy. I need a holiday.

Not many Canadians get the chance to visit Japan at all, and if they do, it is normally a one-off visit, limited to big cities. With this in mind, I decide to travel around some more to parts of Japan that visitors don't often see, trying to absorb as much as I can of this still quite alien landscape. I book a plane to Miyako-jima, a tiny island 300 kilometres south of Okinawa. After the stifling smog of downtown Kyoto, the tropical scents and climate of the island are a huge relief. It is not long before I discover Caribbean-style deserted beaches and tropical trees with fruit ripe for the picking. After a long wade in the ocean surf, I peer into my camera, testing various angles of the panoramic view before I admit defeat. The waterfront is simply too beautiful to capture.

I sling the camera around my neck and tuck my tripod under my arm. As the setting sun splays my shadow in front of me, I march along the path through the woods toward a village. Upon exploration further inland, I discover an ideal subject: The crumbling temple slouches in a back alley, surrounded by sprawling persimmon trees. A black cat ignores my approach and continues to peer curiously at its shadow, which looms on the wall. Without a moment of hesitation, I begin to set up shots of the worn-out Buddha, contrasting it with the fresh offerings scattered around.

I hear voices from inside the near-ruined building and freeze, anticipating the quick disapproval to which I have grown accustomed in Japan's strictly controlled, xenophobic society. I peer through the window into the unadorned, whitewashed interior. Four women, all old enough to be grandmothers, sit in a circle on the floor. All are clapping. One sings.

The words that reach my ears, as I slide happily to a squat outside the window, are certainly Japanese, but the style of singing and the joy that infuses it bring visions of Africa to my mind. The melody is contagiously enthusiastic, and the untrained voices are completely uninhibited.

It would seem as if latitude and climate trump imported culture in the end. If these people carry Japanese passports, it doesn't make them conform—in the ways that matter—to the mainland workaholic frenzy, the pervasive anxiety and striving. Island life and a subtropical temperature, with the regularity of sunrise and sunset that go with it, make their mark just as surely on Miyako-jima's people. Similarly, the people in my part of Canada share a lot with their circumpolar neighbours—the Sami people of Scandinavia and indigenous Siberians in Russia—in some ways more than they share with southern Canadians. Circadian imperialism might impose a continuous stream of influence over marginalized cultures and their daily schedules, but localized rhythms have something on their side: relevance. As I hum along with the old women and gaze at the Japanese sky, the black cat slinks into my lap and falls asleep.

ELEVEN

clocking in

Much of the work that has been done in the field of circadian rhythms can be applied to maximizing human productivity. If we understand the body clock, we can exploit it or at least be aware of its limitations. In isolation labs around the world, circadian researchers monitor their captive subjects in the service of greater understanding of ourselves. In Europe, Japan and the United States, human guinea pigs submit to preprogrammed lighting conditions and prescribed meals for months, like prisoners, but they generally come out of it all raving about their peaceful and productive time in the hole. Real-world applications come out of these studies every year: Consider the recent finding that "anchor sleep"—at least four hours during the same time period every night—can keep the circadian clock steady even if sleep and activity outside of those critical four hours are uprooted.

Human body clocks are not all set to the same time. In the morning, a college student drags himself into a nine o'clock class twenty minutes late with coffee in hand. He won't understand a word until ten. Meanwhile, the student's dad nods off while reading a book at ten at night and regularly excuses himself early from dinner parties to retire to bed. What's the difference between these two men?

If an experimenter put both men in a constant environment where they could run solely on their internal rhythms, a pattern would emerge. The college student—owl-like—would have a free-running rhythm longer than average, say 24.6 hours long. The dad's schedule—following a larkish habit—would be closer to the time outside, with a body clock that takes perhaps 24.2 hours to complete a cycle. Owls and larks are chronotypes, biological categories that determine a lot about lifestyle. In between are the majority of people, who get up and go to bed at an average time and can be called *hummingbirds*, because they hover and flit between morning and evening more flexibly.

Though genes play a part in the most extreme cases—if someone feels the need to get up at four o'clock every morning, for example, there's likely a genetic explanation—most of the variation in the chronotype spectrum comes from age. Young children are typically larks, but as they reach adolescence they adopt an owl-like rhythm. Then around age twenty the body clock speeds up again and remains relatively constant over the rest of people's lives. A fifty-year-old has the same natural waking time, on average, as a ten-year-old, and the elderly are even more larkish.

Society doesn't always cooperate with the demands of the chronotype. High school seniors are only on their game starting just before noon, but school begins relentlessly at nine (or earlier). Biologically appropriate school times might improve learning during those critical pre-university years. Among working adults, owls lose sleep through the work week, catching up on weekends. Larks do well with office hours but forgo rest on the weekends as dinner parties run late into the wee hours: It's a kind of social jet lag.

Unfortunately for me, at least for the next few months, babies are an exception to the human circadian rule. My son kept standard circadian rhythms when I was pregnant with him, because my daily fluctuating hormones flowed to him, and his circulation increased when I was up and active. As soon as he became his own wailing, kicking being, he adopted a three- or four-hour sleep-wake cycle. Like the rhythms of a heart beating or the ups and downs of breathing, the cycles that rule the infant are *ultradian*, meaning they're much shorter than a day.

His tiny stomach needed frequent topping up—otherwise he would have run out of steam in his sleep. Still, long before he begins sleeping through the night, his body temperature starts the twenty-four-hour cycle it will keep throughout his life. Even when he first sleeps through the night, his immature circadian system won't yet be able to accord with the outside time: Dawn will not reset his clock, so it will freely run, drifting off course as its inaccuracies accumulate. Also, the clocks in each organ aren't synchronized with one another, so they conflict and cancel one another out in their overall effect.

If you want your body to function at its best, you should pay attention not only to what you are doing, but also to when you are doing it. For every activity, there is an ideal biological time or, as sleep researcher Josephine Arendt says, "Everything that happens in our bodies is rhythmic until proved otherwise." Brain functions such as alertness, memory, concentration and learning speed rise and fall by up to 30 percent over the course of a day. Internal fluctuations can be exploited to maximize productivity—timing is everything. Intellectual performance, for example, roughly follows alertness, which rises steadily through the day from the moment your alarm-clock grogginess clears to the evening drop that signals bedtime. The opposing force to this expanding capacity is fatigue, which also builds throughout the day. The ability to perform complex tasks tends to peak earlier because fatigue hasn't set in yet, but the ability to complete simple ones follows body temperature's upward slope through the day.

The first half hour after waking is a cognitive train wreck— you'd be smarter if you hadn't slept at all or were legally drunk. In the 1950s, the U.S. Air Force experimented with keeping pilots ready in their planes on the tarmac at all hours. When they were needed at short notice, they'd be awoken for take-off. Accident rates skyrocketed as groggy pilots fought off sleep inertia and, in the end, the military scratched the idea. For those of us who use a cup of coffee in the morning to avoid our own mental crashes, we're better off sipping coffee slowly, a couple of ounces every hour, rather than gulping down a jumbo latte first thing. The gradual drip fights fatigue and buoys cognitive function.

The first mental skill to peak in the morning is short-term memory. A telephone number is better retained—for the time it takes to dial it—in the morning. Later on, a higher body temperature might interfere with those stored numbers, blurring their clarity. Between ten and noon, most of us are capable of our most focused attention. We can concentrate on complex problems and grapple with logical-reasoning tasks. After this, distractions are harder to resist and we become mentally lazy, taking shortcuts to solutions. A slight distractibility might be useful, however, for creative flexibility. It's not just about striving toward excellence; attention to timing can also mean averting disaster. Consider the fact that our tolerance for alcohol fluctuates wildly, with the liver's ability to detoxify the system peaking at around six o'clock in the evening.

What we're learning about circadian rhythms suggests an empowering, if bewildering, range of factors that we should be taking into account just to get through the day safely. Add, for example, a sobering statistic to what we now know about alertness and acuity: 80 percent of car crashes arise from driver inattention just a few seconds before the accident.

As if there weren't enough reasons to get the baby on a sane (adult-friendly) schedule, some research suggests that regular sleep routines during infancy carry long-lasting repercussions. One-month-olds who keep their parents awake at night are more likely to show signs of anxiety—worrying about their future— around puberty, according to a study by Tim Monk, director of the Human Chronobiology Research Program at Pittsburgh's Western Psychiatric Institute and Clinic. As with all correlation studies, the cause and effect aren't clearly defined. Maybe anxious personalities are inherent and manifest as sleeplessness in babies and fretting in teenagers. But maybe parents determine their children's mental health to some extent by setting predictable patterns. Until we finger the culprit, it's probably worth trying to teach babies the difference between night and day—or at least to cooperate with the natural development of daily rhythms—by keeping the curtains open through most of the day and refraining from rambunctious play in the wee hours.

The brain's SCN is not fully developed in a newborn, but it isn't long before babies are on a pattern like the rest of us in most ways, led by body temperature, which is the first rhythm to emerge. The rhythmic effects will be weaker, but the body clock starts its lifelong cycle in those first few months. Only at about age

BEDTIME STORY

Are you reading this book to unwind before sleep? Great idea, but for the early technology adopter who might be reading this on an iPad, beware the potentially insomnia-inducing light from the device's bright, full-colour monitor. Insomniacs are advised to use an electronic reader that uses e-paper, like a Kindle or a Sony Reader, which reflects ambient light more than it produces its own.

five will cortisol (the stress hormone) come into play in the daily rhythm, surging just before dawn. Now the system is complete and its patterns are comparable to adult circadian rhythms, with alertness peaking around noon and again at seven at night, and dipping in the wee hours and after lunch.

Ever since clocks became linked to work—and thus to wealth—they have been political. A gold watch is the traditional parting gesture offered by management to celebrate a long-serving worker's retirement from the company. Dig back to the first days of industry, though, and you find this tradition is a remnant of a time when mill workers couldn't bring any kind of clock into the factory, lest they measure the working hours themselves and claim their rightful pay. Owners then were free to rig the factory's clocks to run slower and force employees into longer workdays. The gold watch symbolizes freedom to keep one's own hours, perhaps a redundant message to a retiree.

Clocks have also been the focus of international cooperation, a precondition of the project to standardize time changes across different time zones. Back in the 1860s, New York professor Charles Dowd proposed the adoption of 15-degree-longitude markers for blocks of standardized time, jumping by one hour at each border rather than reflecting the continuous flow of minutes in sync with the Earth's rotation in relation to the sun. What's remarkable about the adoption of this in the 1880s is the fact that American and Canadian governments agreed to set their time zones using Greenwich Mean Time as a baseline marker. Both North American countries, after all, had a complicated history with Britain. But other countries followed suit, demonstrating that all nations can agree on something, more or less. Still, I would submit that the loss of local time—and the sense of being at the centre of our own community's activities—is not without psychological and cultural cost. Traditional knowledge can never be regained once the last generation of knowledge-keepers dies, and a thorough understanding of daily routines and practices qualifies as a cultural treasure worth protecting.

When I saw proponents of Islam and of the Industrial Revolution trying to overlay mismatching templates onto the sun's behaviour in the Arctic, it was clear that the physical environment had much to do with the discrepancy. The bodies of workers will not cooperate physiologically with a long workday if they're attuned to semi-hibernation, after all. In Spain, the main point of conflict is cultural—a question of preserving the tradition of siesta.

The collective effect of our cookie-cutter timetables produces some odd phenomena. Between eight and nine in the morning, New York City's sewage system feels the effect, known as the Big Flush. A tidal wave of human waste—150 million gallons, up from the 70-million-gallon hourly average—floods the sewer tunnels. It's circadian biology en masse (the Super Bowl halftime surge is apparently a myth).

🕐

Foreign schedules are increasingly imposed, even in Western Europe. A prime example is in Spain, where the siesta is likely to become a casualty of globalization. The siesta, a long nap or quiet time in the early afternoon, translates from the Latin *hora sexta*, "the sixth hour." Assuming the first hour starts at dawn, the sixth falls around noon, and at that point Spain—along with Latin America—tends to shut down for a good three or four hours before resuming activity. Although the siesta often is associated with a leisurely, if not self-indulgent way of life, it's part of a pattern that actually extends the work day into the late evening.

I arrive at my holiday rental house in Almuñécar, an hour outside of Malaga, Spain, on foot. The car is parked down on the main street beside one of the innumerable beauty salons in town, plastered with pin-ups of hair models. From there, the route is a narrow canyon between whitewashed houses, each one differentiated from the next only by the colourful tiling that forms the lower few feet of siding. Scooters whip around blind corners. Children's shouts and soccer balls ricochet from other alleys in the warren. Three flights up from street level, I emerge onto the rooftop terrace to find a parallel city of patios. A silver-haired lady on a roof across the street un-pins from a clothesline a row of home-sewn baby clothes, then hoists three pairs of enormous beige underwear to dry.

This is a Spanish village that still incorporates the siesta into its daily routine. The town square at two in the afternoon suggests a recent apocalypse. The stores are closed; the windows are shuttered, but a child's rocking toy still bobs in the stillness as if recently abandoned. Here in the Costa Tropical in the tourist off-season, siesta is alive and well. The municipal pool is closed from noon to four, and restaurants aren't busy with supper customers until nine at night.

There's a lot of biological support for this kind of after-lunch snooze. Firstly, the body responds to food by succumbing to a decided lull in glucose levels—called a *post-prandial dip*—while the meal is digested. During the energy low after lunchtime, bodily functions slow down and the mind drifts into drowsiness. It's no coincidence that Spanish eaters pack most of their calories into a heavy lunch, provoking a rush of energy-robbing insulin. Even without that food in our stomachs, we go through a drowsy time scheduled after noon by our circadian rhythms. It's likely our prehistoric ancestors took a siesta of sorts to avoid the midday African heat—such a long nap that we've been described as naturally polyphasic, with two innate sleep times serving two different purposes: one to protect us from overheating and sun exposure, and one to restore our body through rest.

Spanish heat can be just as debilitating to productivity as the furnace-like conditions of the African savannah at noon, so the commercial sector defers its efforts until the evening chill sweeps the cobwebs from workers' minds and sharpens their focus. Particularly in urban centres, however, the custom of shutting down for an afternoon siesta is causing problems.

A pan-European company can meet with its Spanish division only during the mornings. After that, office hours never coincide, which becomes a pain in the neck, particularly where continuous cross-border communication can make or break a multinational corporation. Executives aren't used to being told people can't be available for a three o'clock conference call, and if the executives are not culturally educated, they might even attribute the Spanish office hours to laziness.

Though I'm not one for following the prescribed sightseeing itineraries, I couldn't pass up a chance to see the Alhambra while staying in Andalusia. The vast palace complex was built to house the area's Muslim rulers in the fourteenth century and features elaborate gardens, fountains and domes, all in the Arab architectural style of the old Emirate. (As it happens, a favourite pastime in my family is a board game of the same name, whose aim is to construct an Alhambra of grander proportions than that of your opponent.) It is pouring rain when I step between the columns of the palace and confront the vaulted red-grey ceiling. Incredibly detailed arabesques form fractal patterns that, in the most sheltered corners, still bear the blue and white paint of the original building. It's hard to reconcile this grandeur with the lifestyle of the modern Spaniards living in the vicinity. In the 1300s, what we think of as a siesta had not yet entered the picture here. Advocates of reform claim the siesta is hardly an ancient ritual—they assert that it probably began in the 1930s, during the Spanish Civil War when Spaniards would work two jobs, eating a late lunch between them.

So the country has begun a slow, excruciating process of abandoning its distinctive rhythms. In 2006, the federal government officially scrapped the siesta and limited lunches to one-hour blocks, moving the end-of-business hour forward to six o'clock. Barcelona and Madrid have seen the largest private-sector effects, since workers there have more incentive to go along with the changes: Driving out to the sprawling city's suburbs for lunch is no longer practical. As part of the modern urban lifestyle, which often promotes a greater role for fathers in raising children and increased participation by women in the workplace, employees with families would rather take a shorter midday break to avoid returning home at eight or nine at night.

In contrast, smaller cities like Seville and Cordoba in the south have proved stubbornly resistant to the change. When a company tries to convert its workday away from the Spanish custom, employees' unions milk the management for every kind of compensation they can get. Workers argue they no longer have time to return home for lunch, so their employers are often obliged to hand out meal vouchers every day for more expensive restaurant meals.

Spanish workers may be adjusting their commuting behaviour— refusing to travel back and forth for lunch when the distance to the suburbs exceeds a critical point—in a predictable pattern. Marchetti's Constant, based on the work of systems analyst Cesare Marchetti, states that people will spend an hour and a half travelling each day, on average. Even though our ability to travel, as a species, has revolutionized our lifestyles, we still spend the same amount of time travelling every day as our Neolithic ancestors did. Same goes for medieval times. We just go farther in that same amount of time now.

A short walk from Spain, across an airplane runway that serves as a border, brings me to another place where the siesta has little influence. I'm having lunch with an old school friend in Gibraltar, the British territory within sight of Africa, whose giant rock and resident monkeys are its defining features. My friend moved to the area because of a tax law that favours online gambling businesses and the like. The six-square-kilometre peninsula also attracts the global uber-rich, who can claim special status and pay vanishingly low income tax. I spend the afternoon browsing the local shopping area—everything open, everything more English than in England—before heading back to my cosy Spanish *casa*.

An organization called the National Association of Friends of the Siesta made a stand in favour of the tradition in 2011 when they organized a week-long event in Madrid. The first annual Siesta Championship saw about fifty contestants per day lined up in beds in public. Some clutched teddy bears and wore pajamas; others sported eye masks to block the light. Competing for a €1,000 prize, the nappers tried to sleep for a full twenty minutes, monitored by pulse readers. Extra points for costume, original sleeping position and loudest snore kept things fun and interesting. In the end, a sixty-two-year-old unemployed Ecuadorean security guard named Pedro Soria Lopez took the award, his seventy-decibel snore adding a crucial edge to his excellent seventeen-minute snooze.

TWELVE

pushing the limits

Humans have a deeply ingrained propensity for pushing the body's limits. If our key trait is to alter our environment using our intelligence, the body itself is our most immersive environment and no exception to the drive for manipulation. Just as we create artificial worlds to live in—heated houses, brightly lit shopping malls—we endeavour, increasingly, to create more convenient bodies with which to achieve our goals.

Biogerontologist Dr. Aubrey de Grey is a striking figure on the Cambridge scene, both for his chest-length beard and for his single-minded dedication to the problem of aging. His foundation is named SENS, after what it seeks: strategies for engineered negligible senescence—in other words, the end of aging. The object is to eradicate the existing relationship between how old you are and how likely you are to die within the next year. What can I say: I admire ambition.

De Grey proposes that, just as a vintage car can be maintained to run indefinitely, so can the human body, if we adopt a maintenance approach to it. Metabolism, which keeps us alive, creates various types of damage—buildups of junk, mutations, cell loss and the like—that are harmless for a very long time, until they reach a threshold at which they cause pathology. Better than messing around in geriatrics with metabolic processes, which we don't fully understand, intervening to reverse the damage is our best shot at extending human life. This is the stage between being alive and being dead at which we can have maximum leverage—the years before the "frailty threshold" where deterioration becomes disease.

If we develop therapies that reverse cellular damage even partially, patients would buy themselves time (a sixty-year-old becomes biologically fifty, for example) to wait for refined technological advances to extend their lives yet further. De Grey calls this first phase *robust rejuvenation* and proposes that it will add thirty years to the current world age record of a hundred and twenty-two, and it's what he's focusing on, trusting the rest will take care of itself. "The first thousand-year-old is probably less than twenty years younger than the first hundred-and-fifty-year-old," he says. De Grey describes a state—akin to immortality—called *longevity escape velocity*, the event of which he names the *methuselarity* (a blend of *singularity* and *Methuselah*, the almost-thousand-year-old biblical character).

While he admits the task is hard, he insists it is not ridiculously hard. Reasonable critics have chided him for predicting that proof of concept for some of these treatments is only twenty-five years away in mammals. De Grey concedes he may be optimistic about the timeline, but contends that, even so, it *is* only a matter of time. He travels the world evangelizing (his word, not mine) to get funding together and shorten that time.

The not-so-reasonable critics are the ones who most interest me, namely the ones who argue that defeating aging is not desirable. I think these people can be found at any critical juncture in human history, so they're worth studying. Citing the potential problems of an indefinite lifespan—fewer children because of population management, boredom, political and cultural stasis—they suggest that the goal is not worthy of pursuit.

Of course things would be different: People would make decisions based on the anticipation of a long life, for example. Causes of death that have nothing to do with aging would take on a graver significance (de Grey has retracted a former prediction that we would outlaw cars altogether under such circumstances). Innovation and scientific progress, both of which depend on a turnover of fresh faces to create new paradigms, might need other ways to avoid entrenched dogma.

It doesn't take much of a mental leap to accept that not giving future generations the option to buy time—effectively condemning hundreds of thousands per day to a miserable, slow death by aging—might be immoral. As de Grey puts it, losing one's faculties and agility is simply "not as fun" as being healthy and active. He explains the naysayers' behaviour as a natural reaction to the assumption that death is inevitable. Their coping mechanism is to proclaim that they'd rather die after eighty-odd years than live any longer and that they'd just hate to be immortal. An analogous crowd feels similarly about sleep.

"There are some who would choose to run uninterrupted around the clock," writes Jennifer Ackerman, author of *Sex, Sleep, Eat, Drink, Dream*. "But I can't imagine pressing on relentlessly through day and night with mind, body, spirit in a single state, can't imagine denying myself the possibility of a fresh start." This camp tends to say that they relish sleep—it's one of their favourite things to do.

I wonder whether, given that we don't consciously experience most of our sleep time, they actually most enjoy the absence of fatigue. Perhaps it's the lying down and relaxing they enjoy, or the feeling of losing consciousness. I can accept those as experiences of value, but what I have difficulty imagining is waking up to realize the world has gone on without me for eight hours and feeling my heart lift. I'd like the opportunity to decide whether to rest or to go on doing whatever I'm enjoying at that moment, and biology does not allow that to happen. A third of our life is a lot of living to give up involuntarily, but sleep is unlike death in some respects. Where for a secular person, death is simply the absence of life, sleep is more than just not being awake. There are restorative, growth and memory processes actively to be achieved. Until we fully understand the various functions of sleep, we won't be able to "cure" or curtail it in a healthy way. If de Grey's argument is solid, robustly ending the need for sleep would be well worth the challenge, as it achieves the equivalent of a thirty-year waking-life extension.

Wherever nature sets a limit, you can bet there will be humans pushing it. And eight hours a day, a third of one's life, lost to an activity whose reasons are poorly understood—that's a doozy of a limitation. Science fiction is unmoored from bodily restrictions, and it reveals our modern lust for productivity and freedom from sleep. Science-fiction writer Nancy Kress nails the societal resentment of sleep in her Hugo and Nebula Award–winning *Sleepless* series: Genetically engineered children have no need for sleep and no side effects—bucking the science-fiction convention of punishing new technologies through dark consequences. The appeal of an extra eight hours a day is heightened by the fact that only a few humans in her novels possess this advantage, which becomes an unstoppable competitive edge. Catering to her fan base, Kress has the sleepless fortunates using their powers to study all night and become supergeniuses. Not subjected to the brain-stem bombardment that sleepers suffer at night, the sleepless in her novels are emotionally calmer and more stable. The genetically engineered minority becomes a ruling class over the Beggars (those poor mere mortals who still have to sleep). A kind of apartheid develops, with the productive overlords living in guarded compounds.

I catch Kress in her last few days in Rochester, New York, before she moves to Seattle. Now in her mid-sixties, she started writing at age thirty, while expecting her second son. In a rural setting with a toddler at home, she hadn't too many options. "It was either that or soap operas," she says. "And there are some things to which one does not descend." Since then, she's published twenty-five books. The *Sleepless* series was written out of jealousy of friends of hers who needed only six or fewer hours of sleep per night and so accomplished more than she, who needed a good nine hours to feel fresh. Kress admits to me that she tried Modafinil once at a conference in order to stay up and party. Though it kept her awake as planned, the drug left her jittery and upset her stomach—the very properties of the caffeine it is billed as helping you avoid. One of her sleepless characters wanted to experience sleep so badly she injected Interleukin-1, which induces slumber. Kress vividly describes the slipping away of consciousness that results—one of her favourite parts of an otherwise resented need for sleep.

She's confident genetic modification of humans, though currently illegal, will inevitably become accepted, but that it will always be expensive and exclusive. Remembering the editorial outrage directed at 1978's first test-tube baby, Louise Brown, she describes the process whereby reproductive technology creeps forward. It has already started in fertility clinics where couples select fertilized embryos that do not carry the genes for specific heritable diseases. Next will come the option to choose between a baby boy and a baby girl, then to choose taller children.

Finally, we will use the gene-knockout technology we've already been practising for many years on mice. We'll delete a gene that codes for something undesirable and replace it with its advantageous equivalent. So I can learn about one of these genes we might manipulate, Kress directs me to the recent work of Dr. Ying-Hui Fu of the University of California, San Francisco. Fu's lab discovered a gene mutation in humans—and subsequently replicated the finding in mice and fruit flies—that results in shorter sleeps for life. They published their results in the prestigious journal *Science* in August 2009.

A mother and her adult daughter, subjects of the study, had always needed six hours or less of rest per night. They'd typically gone to bed around 10:30 P.M. and woken without alarm clocks at 4:30 A.M., refreshed and hot to trot to the day's activities. It came to light that they shared a rare genetic mutation on the gene DEC2, a *transcriptional repressor*, which means it switches off another gene or genes. While it's not yet known how the genetic mutation translates into sleeping less, and whether the mother and daughter truly get a biological free lunch in this case, the existence of such a variation is promising. A gene like this might be one of the most advantageous genetic endowments a future couple could add to their child. As modern mothers have their children later in life and often struggle to conceive, fertility clinics are booming. It's a short step toward the world of Kress's characters.

Canonical science-fiction writer Ursula K. Le Guin—Kress's hero—also explores the implications of a society that sleeps differently. In her 1976 novel *The Word for World Is Forest*, she populates a planet with little green men who become slaves to the human colonizers. The extraterrestrial beings take a few naps during the day to fulfill their slow-wave sleep requirements, then go into lucid dreaming periodically and at will for their REM sleep. When their masters try to prevent the unproductive "daydreaming," the ETs suffer mentally and physically from the REM deprivation. Beyond their use as inevitable fictional devices, the implications of a sleepless society are worth considering, if only because the newest generations of wakefulness drugs make the possibility more immediate.

We needn't look as far as speculative fiction to find bizarrely immersive artificial environments in which human body clocks are forced to function.

Sometimes, rather than impose an unnatural schedule on a regular solar day, we have to create a sense of normality in the absence of day and night cues. In August 2010, thirty Chilean miners were trapped underground after a section of tunnel was blocked off by a rock fall. While rescue crews dug to find them, their basic needs were being lowered to them, down 700 metres, through bore holes. NASA was on the scene, applying lessons learned over decades of small teams working in the space station or on shuttles.

The living area was divided into three parts—a brightly lit waking area, a darkened sleeping area and a working area. There was some concern that the battery-powered lamps in the waking and working areas, though bright enough to read and work by, would not be bright enough to fully stimulate the circadian system and synchronize their body clocks (activating melanopsin receptors to signal the SCN in the way that sunlight would at dawn). Custom-designed LED lights were sent down by Lighting Science Group Corp., an American company. Miners were advised to start a regular schedule and to supplement their diets with the vitamin D they couldn't take from the sun. Once their nutrition was back on course—they'd lost an average of twenty-odd pounds each while waiting to be found—they stuck to an exercise program on top of their mining work. The key to their success was strict implementation of protocols—rather than waking up a sleeping colleague when a fresh meal had been prepared or taking the day off from their make-work projects, the crew followed instructions to the letter and thrived as a result.

Their triumphant return to the surface after two months led to talk of lucrative film and book contracts, but the field of circadian rhythms is also indebted to them for a rare, real-world demonstration of circadian functioning in a totally artificial environment.

THIRTEEN

dying to sleep

If you watched the Vancouver 2010 Olympics gold-medal hockey game between Canada and the United States, you may have heard what seemed like booing at times when the home crowd should have been cheering. The *boo* sounds were actually a droning chant of "Luu! Luu!" referring to Team Canada's star goalie Roberto Luongo as he made another save. Luongo's regular team, the Vancouver Canucks, had vacated their stadium for the Olympics and incorporated their exile into the longest road trip in National Hockey League history—six weeks and fourteen games, with a two-week break in between so that Luongo and other Olympic selectees could return to the West Coast and bring home the gold.

The Canucks, a West Coast NHL team that's never won the Stanley Cup, took the problem of jet lag and player fatigue very seriously. The team hired Fatigue Management International to analyze their rest patterns on the road. The team members wore what looked like black watchbands during a two-week trip. The wristbands were actually biorhythms bracelets that tracked sleep and energy levels, transmitting heart rates to a recording device, and they were worn at all times, excluding during the team's six away games and during practices.

The primary goal was biofeedback—letting players know what their average sleep time was and when they would have been most fatigued, so they could make their own correlation with how they felt about their performance. Beyond education, the results guided decisions about roommate pairings, practice times on the road and flight-time bookings. The information allowed coaches to assign rooms to players with similar circadian profiles. Practice sessions could be timed to coincide with peak energy and alertness. When games end at 10 P.M., a player eats even later and then wants to wind down before sleep, so there's not much room for compounded effects from jet lag or socializing. The program led to a few players being taken aside and talked to about what might be affecting their play and to reassignment of light sleepers away from snoring roommates.

Fatigue Management International is one of a growing number of companies making a niche out of circadian and sleep dysfunction in a workplace setting. For long-haul drivers, drowsiness is an occupational hazard, so the company has developed a gadget for truckers that plugs into the cigarette lighter of a truck and mounts on the dash. The Driver Fatigue Monitor consists of a camera and a computer that together detect slow eyelid closures. A warning display reads the number of seconds the driver's eyes were closed for, and an alarm sounds roughly an hour before the driver is at serious risk of an accident.

Intuition tells me that if a driver's eyes are closed for more than a second, he or she is already likely in a dangerously drowsy state, but apparently one- or two-second eye closures last for one or two hours before the driver is really asleep at the wheel. Before this final stage, the driver's eyes might be closed for a third or half the time, without him or her realizing the extent of impairment. To put that in context, a truck rolling at 100 kilometres per hour will travel more than a hundred metres during a four-second eye closure. It's not a perfect system: The Driver Fatigue Monitor works only in the dark, during nighttime drives at speeds of over 50 kilometres per hour when drivers are well on their way on the highway. At lower speeds, their heads have to turn at intersections and such, interfering with the monitor—and it'll give a false warning if drivers take their eyes off the road for long, during mirror checks and the like.

Long-distance drivers who, for all intents and purposes, make money according to how far they can drive without stopping, often develop problems with stimulants. Amphetamines are a popular crutch, and cocaine is often available through the grapevine.

Of course, pharmacology is sometimes a legitimate resource for those who have no other option but to stay awake. Our modern dependence on stimulants pushes this idea of necessary chemical pep to the limits—tea, coffee and caffeine-laden pop and energy drinks, even chewing gum and cigarettes are all used to stay alert in what has become a ubiquitous aspect of a sleep-deprived society.

The website for Nuvigil, one of the latest pharmacological products on the market, is a sunny yellow. A construction worker raises his hands in triumph over his newly defeated shift-work fatigue. Along with Modafinil and a handful of others, Nuvigil is a *eugeroic* (Greek for "good arousal") drug. That means it can have alertness benefits similar to those of caffeine or amphetamines without the jitters or comedown side effects of either. In the grand tradition of American drug companies, the makers offer a seven-day free trial to any customer who can badger his or her doctor into writing a prescription. Web surfers can share their Nuvigil stories or take a quiz to find out how sleepy they are before they try the drug. It's a lot of marketing hype for a drug that markets itself. The United States is a nation in which the nonbeing of sleep is an insult to the ego's demands of continual self-assertion.

The United States also has a military that has honed the skills of a nocturnal predator—stealth, power and night vision. Primarily a night-fighting force, the army has routinely counteracted its personnel's circadian rhythms, first through amphetamines and then, reportedly, Modafinil in the more recent wars.

More traditional drugs for alertness include cocaine, which has a long history as a way for humans to circumvent the demands of their circadian system. A psychologically addictive substance that ruins lives, it is now seen as a temptation that leads users away from a productive, honest life. At the turn of the century, during Prohibition, people believed much the same thing about alcohol. Let's take a look at what they were saying back then about coke: "Cocaine makes the coward brave, the silent eloquent, and renders the sufferer insensitive to pain," ran an ad for cocaine tablets sold at the English high-end department store Harrods. Until 1914, there was an enormous legitimate market for cocaine cigarettes, chocolates, tonics and nasal sprays.

Archaeological sources indicate that coca leaves were chewed by people in what is now Peru as early as 3000 BCE. The coca plant was used during religious rituals and burials. By the time the Spaniards arrived in the sixteenth century, the Inca were using it to increase stamina in their workers. The natives of the Andes still chew the unprocessed leaves for their stimulating effect. The habitual chewer, however, has an unsteady gait, green-crusted teeth, incurable insomnia and general apathy.

First synthesized from coca leaves in 1859, cocaine was adopted by the medical community, but its medical use was quickly restricted to local anaesthesia. (This effect is still known to modern users as a numbing in their mouth.) In 1883, the Bavarian army pioneered cocaine's non-medicinal use. Dr. Aschenbrandt administered the coke and found that it boosted the soldiers' endurance. Then he published his findings in a German medical journal—and who should pick up that medical journal but Sigmund Freud. Freud tried the stuff and became the first celebrity cokehead, paid by both rival brands, Merck (the originators) and Parke, Davis to endorse their products, performing clinical studies for them and extolling the benefits of the drug. In 1884, Freud published the paper "Über Coca," giving the drug credit for a great deal of his own accomplishments.

Meanwhile, Coca-Cola came out with its brain-tonic drink, laced with coca extract. The temperance movement embraced it as a virtuous alternative to alcohol. Until 1903, each bottle of Coca-Cola contained an invigorating sixty milligrams of blow. Today, Coca-Cola imports eight tons of coca leaves from South America every year, from which they extract a nonpsychoactive flavouring ingredient. Caffeine provides the kick. Coca-Cola also extracts cocaine for sale to a pharmaceutical company in Missouri for medical purposes.

The combination of cocaine and alcohol was as classy in the 1890s as it isn't now. The Pope himself, along with Queen Victoria and Thomas Edison, preached the benefits of Vin Mariani, a.k.a. cocaine-spiked wine. The fictional character Sherlock Holmes mainlined both cocaine and morphine and then had crucial insight into whatever mystery was on his desk.

The fun couldn't last forever, and in 1914, the U.S. federal government classified coke as a narcotic (in America, the term refers to a prohibited substance, rather than a sleep-inducing one—still the definition of *narcotic* in the rest of the world) and outlawed its use outside of a prescription. So with blow illegal, users pretty much abandoned it in favour of speed, which was still accepted. After all, speed lasts longer and it was cheap and, best of all, legal. Amphetamines (including methamphetamine, another variant of speed) were banned in 1960, and speed users switched back to coke. That's how the first flurries of the current cocaine blizzard began. Interest in cocaine mounted when, in 1976, freebase—a smokable, non-water-soluble form—was developed in California. Supply from South America rose eagerly, and the price fell steadily from $55,000 per kilogram wholesale in 1981 to just under $25,000 in 1984. Crack (freebase cocaine) smoking began in the dealer ranks, where the faster effects of smoking the drug allowed coke distributors to test the purity of the merchandise before they bought it from manufacturers. Then crack became the drug with the most bang for the buck. As new street drugs and mainstream pharmaceuticals develop, one thing is certain—there will always be a place for shortcuts to energy and wakefulness. And there will always be a rebellious cachet in staying up all night, whether for work or for play.

⏰

Avoiding sleep is such a challenge because of how much sleep is a part of us, hard-wired and necessary for our body's functioning. Sleep, in one form or another, is a vertebrate universal and dates back to the nighttime metabolic processes of our ancestral organisms, designed to protect them from harmful ultraviolet rays. Though human sleep drifts through stages—*theta wave, slow wave, rapid eye movement*—the transition from being awake to being asleep is a sudden switch in the brain's hypothalamus. Sometimes it might be too rapid—if you've ever been on the brink of sleep, but spasmed awake with a falling sensation, it may have been your body's reaction to a sudden drop in breathing and heart rate. Called the *myoclonic jerk*, that spasm happens when the largest muscles in the body contract quickly as *atonia*, or loss of motor control, begins. It's much easier to fall asleep in the late evening when melatonin has been circulating and the pressure for sleep has been building. The higher your body temperature, the harder it is to get to sleep, which accounts for insomnia caused by upset feelings or excitement, which keep the body warm.

We know that bad things happen when we don't sleep: Rats deprived of sleep die faster than they would of starvation. A poor night's sleep each night for a week leads to cognitive deficits as bad as those after pulling an all-nighter, and sleep-deprived people often fall into microsleeps (three-to-ten-second noddings-off) for a few seconds at a time. In the most extreme case—Fatal Familial Insomnia—an unfortunate set of genes leads to a buildup of *prions* (the kind of proteins implicated in mad cow disease). In their early fifties, victims suddenly stop sleeping altogether. First their blood pressure and pulse rise, and their pupils shrink to dots over the course of a week. After months they can't walk or speak, and they eventually fall into an exhausted coma and die.

But knowing what happens when we don't sleep is not the same as knowing *why* we sleep. If the function of sleep is to stop us from being tired, the argument falls into tautology. University of Chicago sleep expert Allan Rechtschaffen has called it the biggest open question in biology because of the severe survival disadvantages of shutting off the brain for hours every day. "If sleep does not serve an absolutely vital function, it is the greatest mistake that evolution ever made," he writes. "While we sleep, we do not procreate, protect or nurture the young, gather food, earn money, write papers, etc. ... There is something tremendous out there, and we just haven't found it."

Two broad functions—repair and growth, and memory consolidation—present themselves in the form of two sleep types: slow wave and REM. Each night, sleep alternates every ninety minutes between REM, a brain pattern similar to wakefulness, and slow wave, when cortical activity cuts down to less than three cycles per second (an alert brain can cycle forty times per second). The first two ninety-minute cycles of the night are dominated by slow-wave sleep, which is recuperative and sees the infusion of growth hormones into the blood stream and a lot of tissue repair.

Later in the night, as body temperature drops yet further, REM fills in a bigger part of the cycle. It accounts for a quarter of the total sleep time. Perched at the edge of waking, REM may have evolved from a time when our ancestors had to get up to scout for danger and changing weather patterns every hour or so. Dreaming may be our body's way of fooling us into staying asleep. REM is where dreaming happens and learning solidifies. If you learned something new the day before, REM sleep will activate the same parts of the brain you used in that task and you'll be better at it tomorrow, as if you'd practised. Students should take their cue from babies, who spend eight hours a day in REM sleep processing and storing information, and streamlining the efficiency of their brain connections. It pays to be well rested before class, but it's just as important to sleep on it afterward. During dreaming your body is paralyzed, and your forebrain—responsible for planning and decision-making—shuts off, leading to associative dream logic. If you're faintly aware of the motor-control loss, you might have one of those dreams where you're running away from something scary, but your legs won't quite run properly.

Herbivores sleep less than carnivores because their food-gathering takes up so much time and is less efficient. Carnivores score a big meal, and then doze for much of the day—like domestic cats of a certain age, lethargic in their food security. Humans, being omnivores, are somewhere in the middle. Within those categories, larger animals with slower metabolisms tend to sleep less, suggesting sleep might be for repairing the cell damage that's a by-product of metabolism.

Advantageous as a way to keep higher vertebrates inactive during the hours for which they are least well-adapted, sleep has also taken on the burden of various brain functions. When body temperature drops for sleep, it's a perfect opportunity for the brain to restock proteins, strengthen synapses and generally catch up on its housekeeping. The lower brain temperature minimizes interference by slowing chemical processes, thereby letting the neurons do their internal work more efficiently.

Slow-wave sleep concentrates the body on cellular regeneration. REM sleep consolidates learning. Psychiatrists have used these separate functions to develop a treatment for depression: Depriving a patient selectively of REM sleep, when serotonin systems are shut down, seems to work as an antidepressant, probably because there's more feel-good serotonin available during waking time. If depressed people are allowed to sleep without interference afterward, though, they'll spend a greater proportion of their night dreaming than they would otherwise—apparently selectively making up for REM sleep deprivation. Same goes for slow-wave sleep deprivation, in the other direction.

The onset of sleep entails a series of steps. For normal sleepers on regular schedules, sleepiness still asserts its presence to some extent throughout the day. Every hour and a half we get a wave of sleep pressure. Each pulse of tiredness is stronger than the last, the further away your last sleep was. On the other hand, the SCN sends out stronger and stronger alertness signals to combat fatigue until late evening, when it abruptly packs it in and we succumb to exhaustion. In the middle of the day, when the SCN's influence is still weak and there is already some accumulated sleep deprivation, we feel the post-prandial dip. It's so named because it usually happens just after lunch and is exacerbated by an insulin surge that results in sugar being removed from the bloodstream. There's a spike in single-vehicle accidents—caused by drivers falling asleep at the wheel—between one and four in the afternoon, as well as the more intuitively predictable one-to-four-in-the-morning peak. This is also when bus and railway accidents are most likely to happen, their drivers momentarily groggy, leading to mass casualties.

Napping has been proven effective in relieving grogginess and the bad mood, low productivity and lack of alertness that go with it—even for people who report feeling even more tired after a nap (a phenomenon known as *sleep inertia*, whereby there are residual effects from the sleeping state). Pilots who nap during long flights—implementing plans that rely on co-pilots to take over the cockpit—improve their reaction times and fall into fewer microsleeps during the landing phase of flight, which is the most dangerous time in a long flight shift.

Regular maintenance of a healthy body clock requires awareness of best practices in the area of sleep hygiene. No matter whether you're a morning lark or a night owl, lots of time spent out of doors advances the cycle. That is, everyone becomes more larkish if they get plenty of fresh air and, more to the point, sunshine. To me, this suggests society has become progressively more prone to staying up late as artificial light has become available, and many have been able to accommodate it within their biology. It also supports the notion that pre-industrial people probably slept shortly after dusk and woke at dawn (with or without the mysterious midnight waking hours).

When chronobiologists try to shift the body clock to a new time zone just by changing sleeping hours—making their subjects sleep from one to nine in the morning, say—without changing the light environment, they have little success. The first light still floods the room and resets the clock. Unless dawn happens later too, sleeping patterns alone are not enough to reset internal clock to a later time. In scientific language, sleeping times are a weak *zeitgeber*, and light remains the strongest time cue of all.

Of course, the light environment—as far as the brain is concerned—gets darker during sleep because the eyes are closed, so often sleep-schedule changes amount to changes in light input and do indeed shift body clock cycles either earlier or later. As a consequence of this, staying up later than usual has less effect than waking up later than usual: Even a regular bedtime falls long after darkness, whereas waking up a couple of hours later usually means missing a significant chunk of daylight time. The American National Sleep Foundation has been formalizing this research into recommendations, such as refraining from sleeping in on the weekend so that Monday's reversion to work hours doesn't cause more sleep deprivation than it needs to. While recognizing the central problem—proliferating work hours—the foundation recommends that people give up the habit of staying up late after a long day's work, and then sleeping in to make up for lost time. The best way to recover from a long week, they say, is to go to bed earlier, and then wake up at a sensible time and take a morning walk outside. More light paired with more sleep makes for real rest and recuperation.

Elderly people have their circadian challenges too. As the body clock ages, it seems to become set to an earlier solar time, waking its owner in the early morning hours. Researchers aren't sure exactly why this happens, but a shrinking SCN, starting around age seventy, is a promising clue. So are age-related changes in the eye. The lenses start to turn yellow, blocking blue light, the key spectrum for the photopigment melanopsin, which is crucial for resetting the body clock. Sleeping less in general, older people often start to suffer from insomnia, complaining that while they can easily fall asleep, it's much harder for them to stay asleep. Their circadian rhythms flatten, so the drop in body temperature is not as profound in the evening and the halt of urine production isn't as complete, leading to trips to the bathroom. Even during sleep they experience anywhere from two hundred to a thousand episodes of microarousal, in which they awake momentarily before falling back into slumber, compared with around a dozen episodes in younger people. The fact that retirement from work gives ample time during the day for napping might only exacerbate the problem by blurring the distinction between day and night. Much better to establish a routine, getting plenty of light in the daytime so there's no confusion about when to sleep.

Long before people start complaining of terrible sleep due to aging, the process starts almost imperceptibly. Early adulthood offers the best chance of a good night's sleep—and the clear mind that follows it—but even by your late thirties and moving into your late forties, less than 4 percent of time in bed is spent in deep sleep. That's a mere fifth of the time enjoyed in deep sleep during the prime of life. It wouldn't be surprising, knowing what we know about sleep and the brain, if this turned out to be the main force behind the cognitive deficits, such as memory difficulties and concentration problems, that accompany normal aging.

In people of all ages, most mild cases of insomnia can be managed through good sleep hygiene: going to bed at a regular time (including on weekends), refraining from naps that might relieve the evening sleep pressure and cutting out nicotine and caffeine. Alcohol, while it might induce sleepiness, will lead to a bad night's sleep in numerous ways—it suppresses the theta waves of stage-two sleep and produces a diuretic effect that will send you to the bathroom in the middle of the night.

Total darkness is important for sleep in many ways. Any light at all can have some effect on how much melatonin the body is able to release, but the consequences can be more dire than a poor night's sleep. Richard Stevens at the University of Connecticut has shown that female shift workers exposed to light in the nighttime are at a much higher risk of breast cancer, probably because melatonin inhibits estrogen, a hormone that's implicated in accelerating breast tumour growth. Lack of proper melatonin infusion at night can lead to chronic fatigue as the sleep hormone's concentration in the bloodstream gets distributed a little more evenly over time, and depression becomes a worry as well. Stevens went on to show that there were similar—though less significant—effects from sleeping in a room with just a little bit of light in it. Maybe the hall light is on and shining under the door. It's hard not to think that light pollution is becoming a bigger issue than just an inconvenience for astronomers: It's bigger than anyone knew.

People who have trouble sleeping often turn to sleep aids, and although they report falling asleep faster and sleeping for longer, they also describe a kind of drug-induced sleep that isn't fully refreshing. A brilliant study by Wallace B. Mendelson's Sleep Research Laboratory uncovered a clue as to how a sound but low-quality sleep is possible. He took two groups of subjects into the lab for the night, one claiming to be good sleepers and the other claiming to be bad sleepers. After all the subjects had been asleep for ten minutes, according to electroencephalogram recordings, the scientists woke them up and asked them what they were doing—kind of a strange question to get first thing on waking, but their answers were intriguing. The group of good sleepers said, correctly, that they had been sleeping. The bad sleepers denied it.

Then Mendelson gave them all Ambien and tried the same experiment again. The bad sleepers this time reported having been sleeping. It's possible that sleeping pills are most effective at changing the perception of a good night's sleep. Sleeping pills don't necessarily make you sleep; they may just make you *think* you have been sleeping.

Because they have fewer side effects, melatonin supplements are a milder way to train your circadian rhythms by signalling bedtime to the body. Studies of arrhythmic blind people show the tablets to be effective for partially replacing the input of light and dark cycles—at least for a subset of the experimental subjects. Depending on the type of vision impairment, blind people sometimes have intact circadian systems, but sometimes suffer from constant free-running rhythms. Problems tend to be worse if there is comprehensive retinal damage or nerve damage that includes the retinohypothalamic tract, which carries light-level information to the SCN. Internal daily cycles still exist in these patients, but they have no input from the system's main calibrator—the eyes—so these people drift around the clock, finding regular school and work schedules very hard to follow.

While medical circles inch toward accepting the body clock's importance, everyday people have been trying to achieve health through better sleep patterns based on sheer intuition, experimenting with anything and everything that seems to deepen sleep. The first symptom of many serious illnesses is the feeling of being tired all the time. A natural first step is to try to improve sleep quality and quantity. Sleep has become a major industry in the first world.

Las Vegas's big winter 2010 furniture show rolled out the latest in luxury beds, catering to those who believe quality of life starts with quality of rest. Manufactured by Leggett & Platt, the Prodigy is a bed base that elevates by remote control to a different angle on either side of the bed, so one partner can work on a laptop while the other sleeps. If your husband starts snoring, you need only press a special button on the remote and it will raise him to 7 degrees for fifteen minutes—apparently the precise cure for blocked airways. Easing a sleeper into new positions, the bed gently shifts beneath the mattress. Set the bedside alarm (through your iPhone, if you wish) and the Prodigy will bring you into a new day with a massage—even a head massage, if you don't find that thought as creepy as I do. None of this blaring-siren business for the refined set among us. Couples that had great outdoor sleeping experiences at tropical resorts can bring the open-air-bedroom concept home. King-sized gazebo-style canopied platforms bring the breezes through on warm summer nights.

Less adventurous and less decadent bed shoppers have more pedestrian dilemmas on their minds, like the pregnant woman who's running hot, but doesn't want to impose her fluctuating temperature demands on the whole family's thermostat. For those going through such a pregnancy or through menopause—or for those who just prefer a different sleeping environment—Hirakawa Corporation in Japan designed cooling and heating pads with no power requirement. A basic ability to customize each side of the mattress for firmness solves a difference in preference almost half of couples suffer, even if they don't recognize it.

Lately, an inexplicably popular trend has swept the crossword and word-search market. No longer just a pastime for long train rides, puzzles like Sudoku are now marketed as "brain fitness" workouts that help people obtain, if not the physique of a younger self, at least the mind of one. A bestselling computer program—endorsed by a Japanese neuroscientist—puts gamers through a repetitive series of daily tasks to achieve a lower *brain age* (not to be confused with *mental age*). To stave off the effects of aging on cognitive performance, we must exercise our brains and buy lots of stuff, says the world of mind-fitness marketing—never mind the common-sense argument that living a richly social and challenging life, varying your activities and staying physically active is indisputably the best way to keep your mental faculties from atrophy.

Riding on the coattails of this fad is the sleep-fitness industry. Even if you can't afford or geographically access nights of surveillance in private sleep laboratories and clinics, the industry will sell you all manner of gadgetry to give you the experience from home. The self-diagnosis of it all is undeniably appealing. Take the Zeo Personal Sleep Coach, for example, with its 7 Step Sleep Fitness Program. To start, you put on a headband and go to sleep, and when you wake up, the Zeo presents you with a baseline ZQ score. (Get it? It's like IQ, but with Zs and it's a number you're trying to increase for greater sleep fitness.) Sometimes I think there's a huge segment of consumers who miss school, with all its satisfying quizzes and numerical pats on the back. The ZQ is based on sleep time overall as well as on slow-wave and REM time. It comes with a graph showing how long it took you to fall asleep and how much time you spent awake during the night.

Like the Sleep Cycle iPhone app (but for a lot more money), the Zeo will wake you at a light-sleep phase. The main component of it looks a lot like an alarm clock. There's seemingly no end to the time you can spend obsessing over your sleep, with online sleep journals set up for you to record your "sleep-stealers," Zeo worksheets and MP3s, daily relaxation, diet and bedtime routine advice. Then you can upload your data onto the computer for yet more analysis. There's a caveat that the six-month personalized email coaching is not meant to diagnose or combat an honest-togoodness pathology like narcolepsy or sleep apnea. It's more along the lines of suggestions that you keep the dog out of the bedroom. But it's the therapeutic packaging—words like *assessment*, for example—that gives the Zeo an aura of legitimacy and authority.

Of course there's nothing wrong with taking an interest in your own sleep—it's part of what attracts people to the field that is the topic of this book—and if people want to pay hundreds of dollars for a fun package to help them do that, it's their choice. I'd just like them to recognize that it's partly a form of entertainment.

For all the biological and psychological effects of sleep or lack thereof, the sciences don't even begin to cover the true power it exerts in our day-to-day lives. Sleeping can become the focus of interpersonal conflict—and even a hot-button political issue.

I meet sociologist Jenny Hislop for tea to discuss sleep from another perspective. Hislop's work looks at older women and how they sleep. She also explores how couples negotiate sleep between them; she sends me a list of papers with titles like "It's Okay for a Man to Snore." At the cafeteria at Oxford University's Primary Health Care department, Hislop recounts the studies that convinced her that women not only are being shortchanged in society's division of labour but also are getting cheated of their sleep. In "A Bed of Roses or a Bed of Thorns?" she debunks the romantic notion of the double bed after interviewing dozens of couples, aged twenty to sixty, regarding everything that bugged them about sleeping with another person. Keeping a sleep diary and having their sleep times tracked for a week using wristwatch-style devices called *actigraphs*, the couples weighed in on what they felt were the underlying causes of poor sleep. Hislop and co-investigator Sara Arber probed the gendered nature of sleep in our culture.

Just like in any other power struggle, the bedroom becomes a contested space. Couples battle over whether to open or close the window, sleep in total darkness or with a night light, turn down the thermostat or keep the room warm. They nurse grudges about pillows and duvets. Some women want their men on the side close to the door, so they can be protectors, but others want the easy access to the bathroom. Hislop heard tale after tale, things the research subjects had never told anyone else in their lives—the way they hated getting drawn into the gravity well of a heavier partner weighing down the mattress or the hours of sleep lost every night to incessantly snoring husbands. Some had packed it in altogether and claimed their own bedrooms if they were lucky enough to have a second one available, bucking the shared-bed stereotype as the symbol of marriage, but often feeling bad about it.

Spiky-haired with dangly earrings, Hislop has the vestiges of an Australian accent. As an undergraduate in Sydney she studied French and Indonesian language and anthropology before teaching Indonesian in secondary schools. The couples sleep project was the basis of a mid-career doctorate. During a study where women kept free-form sleep diaries for seven nights, Hislop realized that women were taking on emotional labour at night, thinking about their children, devoting mental space to lists of things to do. She found their sleep very disrupted. "When they couldn't sleep, some of them would tell me they got up to do the ironing. Which of course is 'women's work'!" says Hislop. It's worth noting that in this particular study only women were included in the focus group. We have nothing but their reports to tell us that their spouses weren't also lying awake worrying. Perhaps if the men had been included, they would have reported themselves as the losers and night-labourers in many of these sleep battles.

Margaret Thatcher famously proclaimed that sleep is for wimps. Buckminster Fuller maintained that sleep is just a bad habit. Two hours a day is plenty, he said, if it's scattered in half-hour naps every six hours (now known as the Dymaxion sleep schedule). History is replete with lore around celebrity nonsleepers. Salvador Dali is reputed to have balanced a spoon on his hand and slept only until the spoon fell. It seems that whenever a cult of personality develops around a great thinker, politician or artist, the first thing to be embellished is his or her ability to stay awake while weaker mortals sleep.

The reality is that all the greatest nonsleepers share one other thing in common—they're long dead, and we can't verify their schedules. The geniuses in question probably pulled all-nighters during creative manias—fuelling the lore—then crashed for long recuperative sleeps the next day. The same names come up in this stubborn meme as in every list of famous people affected by dyslexia, practising vegetarianism or believing in you-name-it: Franklin, da Vinci, Jefferson, Einstein. Intentionally short sleep for the sake of productivity should not be confused with insomnia, a scourge on stressful living then as now. As Dorothy Parker wrote, "How do people go to sleep? I'm afraid I've lost the knack. I might try busting myself smartly over the temple with the night light." And there's no doubt leadership brings with it sleep deprivation.

Two workaholics, Thomas Edison and his protégé-turned-rival Nikola Tesla, had a contest going for who could sleep less. A naturally short sleeper, Edison believed that humans sleep far more than necessary and called it "a waste of time." Then again, he also didn't think exercise was a worthwhile use of time. Though he didn't sleep much at night, his nap cots, a source of daytime refreshment, have been preserved in museums. Tesla accused Edison of exaggerating his wakefulness.

The great innovators of times past almost certainly got at least a core minimum of sleep, most of the time. We can be confident in this assumption when we see what happens to people who don't. Though they may be able to physically stay vertical and moving, there is not a great deal of creative work being done or many scientific problems being solved among people who are seriously sleep deprived. The internet has seen an explosion of a very appealing meme called the *Uberman polyphasic sleep schedule*, which involves a series of short naps around the clock, with no long periods of sleep at all. When I say appealing, I mean that the lure of extra hours in the day seems to motivate people to the most extreme lengths of self-deprivation in the hopes that they will eventually adjust to it.

Psychologist Piotr Wozniak scans the blogs of people—mostly young men—attempting such an experiment. They usually begin with high hopes: "Goals for 2006: become FULLY polyphasic. Make a million dollars by my birthday," wrote one blogger. Soon there follows a series of bitterly regretted "oversleeping" incidents as the subject slips up on his gruelling schedule: "I kept nodding off in my room because it was dark as my roommate, Phil, is enjoying his crappy monophasic sleep." "My brain really, really wants me to sleep nine hours a day, apparently. Well, screw you, brain." "Today's blog post was a bit ... disturbing. I don't even recall making it."

Wozniak's informal subjects make all kinds of excuses for the fact that they don't seem to be adjusting: "Man, I'm struggling so badly today ... I really pissed my body off. Must have been the popcorn, because I can't think of any other reason for this." And their blogs are rich in dubious theories: "NASA says that twenty-four minutes is the optimal nap time." In the end, each blog concludes with the subjects abandoning the sleep schedule, usually blaming themselves or their circumstances, rather than biological reality. "Polyphasic sleeping is not the most girlfriend-compatible stunt," wrote one young man.

In contrast, biphasic sleep—a slightly shortened core slumber with a short snooze in midday—is eminently workable. Churchill's wartime schedule was well documented and, by all accounts, he was energetic and hard to keep up with. He'd wake at 8 A.M. and read or do correspondence for a while. Following a midday nap, in which he'd fully change into pajamas, he'd work until 3 A.M. Churchill maintained this gave him a day and a half in the place of each day.

Of course, there are tasks that require round-the-clock vigilance, and it is possible to sustain them through short naps only, though not as a long-term lifestyle. Dr. Claudio Stampi is a sailing enthusiast and circadian rhythms expert who trains round-the-world sailboat racers to take a series of catnaps during their weeks-long race, never stopping for a proper rest. Author of *Why We Nap: Evolution, Chronobiology and Functions of Polyphasic and Ultrashort Sleep*, he warns that this waking life is unsustainable. The longest training experiment he conducted lasted forty-nine days—one man sustained himself for the entire duration on a total of three hours of sleep per day.

Long-distance sailors have been pioneers in sleep-deprivation management. The first solo world circumnavigator, Canada's Joshua Slocum, headed out from Boston in 1895, using only dead reckoning to navigate "the seven seas." He experienced several hallucinations before reaching Gibraltar, including a vision of one of Christopher Columbus's pilots aboard his boat. Slocum was feverish at the time, but that mightn't have been the only cause of his vision. Hallucination is a common experience for sailors after several days alone at sea pushing through their duties on a tired brain.

FOURTEEN

2030: a sleep odyssey

While most alternative sleep schedules somehow fit into a twenty-four-hour cycle, NASA spacecraft engineers and scientists sometimes have to work with the system of a planet or setting that cycles on its own rhythm—with more or fewer than twenty-four hours. For the inside scoop, I call up my old friend Miles Smith, a thirty-nine-year-old astrophysicist for NASA's Swift mission, working out of Penn State. In the latest round of astronaut selections, which are performed every four or five years, Smith narrowly missed getting picked from the pool of semifinalists, although, given the whittled-down space program, even the nine selected might not all make it off our planet. Now an American, when Smith first befriended me, he was an Australian post-doctoral astrophysics student freshly back from a winter at Antarctica's Amundsen-Scott South Pole Station, where he served as the resident astronomer. Every day, he would crunch out on the frigid snow in absolute silence and look into the telescope. The South Pole is in every time zone at once, so the station picked one—New Zealand's time—for the purposes of scheduling, though there was no sunlight in winter to wake up to.

As an astronomer, however, Smith lived on *sidereal time*. Instead of getting up every day when the sun has come back around to the same place in the sky—what most of us do—Smith set his watch by the time when a given point in the starscape had moved around to the same spot in his telescope. The difference from our twenty-four-hour clock, around four minutes faster every day, was hardly noticeable in the short run, but his gradual drift away from conventional time meant living out of sync with the rest of the station, the work crews and other scientific personnel. He spent much of his free time reading through the large box of popular-science books he'd lugged down to tide him through winter.

No planes could safely land and take off from the South Pole in winter, so Smith and his teammates were stuck with each other until spring, like it or lump it. Returning home to Australia in spring, he found the local cafés full of jarring noise he could no longer filter out, so silent had been the months in isolation.

Back in those post-doctoral days Smith was going to an astro-biology conference at NASA Ames Research Center at Moffett Field, near Mountain View, California, and he suggested I come along. I weaseled a press pass to the event and hopped on a plane to San Francisco. There, I met Smith and we drove to Ames, where we entered through the guarded gate, under the shadow of a spacecraft hangar the size of a sports stadium. The conference opened with a recorded video message from the then-president George W. Bush, directing NASA to carry out its new series of smaller-scale missions, with the eventual goal of sending humans to Mars.

Here, science fiction met reality, with a debate about terra-forming Mars into a habitable simulacrum of Earth. The debate included Sir Arthur C. Clarke (teleconferencing in from his home in Sri Lanka) and Hugo and Nebula Award–winning sci-fi authors Greg Bear and Kim Stanley Robinson, in dialogue with the leader of the team that built the Mars Pathfinder rover. Groups of exobiologists, who look for life beyond Earth and speculate as to its nature, mingled next to conference posters about the search for extraterrestrial intelligence, and colleagues of the astronauts killed in the recent *Columbia* disaster discussed the way forward. By the end of the conference—I don't know how, but it's just the way he does things—Smith had a job with NASA. He moved down to the Jet Propulsion Laboratory in Pasadena to work on the Phoenix Mars Mission, leading a team that scheduled the scientific operations of the lander, which spent five months on the red planet's northern plains, taking samples and images. From a personal point of view, he became a source of great pride for me, newly a journalist and now with a much-coveted "source at NASA."

Through the summer of 2008, Smith lived in a hotel in Tucson; the University of Arizona was hosting the mission's Science Operations Center, from which the lander was commanded and to which the spacecraft's data was transmitted. He and the rest of the science and engineering team lived on Mars time—24.7 hours in a day—because the lander itself was dependent on the sun to power its solar cells. During prime mission operations, the lander would wake up for a busy day on Mars's North Pole permafrost, and the crew on Earth would be ready at work, waiting to upload its daily commands. There was a lot of digging to do and new experiments to be performed every day. The extra thirty-nine minutes in each day, from the end of May when the spacecraft landed until mid-August, meant that the operations staff missed almost a day every month. They worked with the windows blacked out so as not to get thrown off schedule.

Just as the NASA folks in Tucson were studying Martian soil samples and atmospheric readings, researchers from the Johnson Space Center, which specializes in human space flight, were studying the operational staff themselves. Ground crews living on Martian time during the earlier Mars Pathfinder and Mars Exploration Rover missions had reported problems concentrating, irritability and fatigue. It was a rare opportunity to capture the predicted circadian disruptions, sleep problems and performance decrements in an actual operational setting. In the long run, the project also served as a high-fidelity Mars analogue for some future time when humans might want to live on other planets and would need to adjust to different day lengths. Urine samples were taken for checking melatonin and cortisol levels at various times, and one group was given bright blue light panels for their work areas as a measure to compensate for the lack of sun, to see if the panels might help people adapt to a longer day. Monitors on the subjects' wrists measured light exposure and sleep cycles, and the subjects answered mood and alertness quizzes and underwent vigilance tests. "I was not a good research subject," admits Smith, who found it hard to fulfill the circadian researchers' demands on top of his intense workload planning the Phoenix lander's experiments. It was also different for him, being away from his family, than it was for the other personnel, who were still living at home and distinctly aware of the mainstream time around them.

His was the kind of job where colleagues would offer to pick up lunch for him, knowing he might not otherwise have time to eat. After a ten-hour continuous shift, he'd finish the day exhausted and in no mood for an hour's work of cognitive testing. "Of course, those days when I needed to go home and sleep were exactly the times when they most needed to get their data," he recalls. Still, he contends that nothing beats that kind of intense, exhausting work—you sleep better, wake up fresher, and food even tastes better. The intensive media interaction—a cadre of journalists was often hanging around the operations headquarters—gave him a feeling of being part of something important. In the end, the work was the most important thing, but it did make life exciting to know the world was watching, and he knew the buzz that he thought must accompany athletes at the Olympics.

Both the athletes and the NASA scientists were at the top of their game, in the peak moments of their careers, making history in their respective domains.

Finally, in August, the digging wound down; the lander was running out of power and chemistry cells, so Phoenix became an imaging mission rather than an experimental one. The command centre reverted to Earth time, since instructions could now be sent every two or three days—there was no longer a 25-hour daily deadline to keep them on a Martian schedule.

The Phoenix Mars mission's predecessor—the 1975–76 Viking Mars mission—also contributed to circadian rhythms research. Outer space is the new circadian laboratory, and our discoveries could even lead to a greater understanding of extraterrestrial life forms. Because there was evidence of water on Mars, there was some basis for thinking that there was life, and experiments were devised specifically to test for life. Hotly debated interpretation of the Viking Mars lander data suggests that microbes in the Martian soil revealed themselves at the time through their circadian rhythms—a *biosignature*, or "sign of life." It started with a soil sample. The test added to the soil a liquid solution containing carbon-14, a radioactive form of the element that can then be used as a marker, because it emits radiation wherever it ends up. The *labeled release experiment* assumes that any living organisms could be detected by their absorption of the nutrients and subsequent release of metabolized gas containing the carbon-14. Both the Viking 1 and 2 landers got a positive result on this experiment, welcomed with caution in some quarters and with jubilation in others. Further life-detection experiments came up negative, however, and it was concluded at the time that the labeled release result must have come from some kind of oxidant in the Martian soil. By readily releasing oxygen, these oxidizing compounds would create the illusion of life exhaling the gas.

Of course it pays to be conservative in coming to scientific conclusions, especially when the world's media is itching to elaborate on your highly publicized findings. But circadian biologist Joe Miller of the University of South California refused to take the official record that the result was a "false positive" as the final word—what good is data if scientists won't accept it, after all? Even though the results had come back exactly as predicted in the case of Martian life, Miller analysed the labeled release from another angle.

Carbon-14-labelled gas emerged from the Martian soil sample in a pattern that was expected from microbe-infested dirt. There was a large increase in gas immediately after the nutrients were injected into the soil and a slow rise over the long-term course of the experiment itself. Most telling, clear periodic oscillations emerged with a 24.66-hour cycle—the length of a Martian day. Though not all chemical compounds have been eliminated, Miller maintains that the biological explanation is far more plausible. "In all probability, Viking discovered life on Mars twenty-five years ago [in the 1976 Viking lander data]," he said. The Phoenix lander's reports in 2008 have shed more light on the oxidants in the soil, but one thing's for sure—when it comes to circadian rhythms, little green men will not be as foreign as we imagine. Astrobiologists now speculate about life on other planets with a strong suspicion that organisms on any spinning planet will cycle in some way to the rhythm of that rotation. If there's life on another planet, it should respond to circadian cues.

Until recently, the search for potentially habitable planets has been frustrated by the types of planets we've been finding. The habitable zone is the distance away from a star where water is liquid—in other words, where temperatures vary between 0 and 100 degrees Celsius—and life as we know it could function. The planets we're looking for can't be too small or they won't have enough atmosphere, and they can't be too big or they're likely not to have a solid surface. And their orbits can't be too elliptical or they're likely to stray out of the habitable zone for long enough to kill any life that was starting to form. Though astronomers have found hundreds of planets in other solar systems, using sophisticated telescopes and techniques, those planets have tended to be too big and too close to their suns.

Otherwise known as the Goldilocks Zone (not too hot, not too cold, juuuust right!), the habitable zone has finally offered up a planet twenty light years away from Earth that fits the bill. Publishing their results in the *Astrophysical Journal* in 2010, its finders gush that conditions are ideal for water, though we don't know if there is any. Wherever there is water on Earth, we find life, so one of the authors has gone so far as to say the planet, which orbits around the low-energy dwarf star Gliese 581, has a high probability of containing life. It's still three times more massive than Earth and one-seventh the distance from its sun— Gliese 581—as we are from ours, but its temperatures are equivalent to Earth's.

Accepting, for a moment, the claim that we have just discovered another planet containing life, let's imagine it. This particular planet does not rotate much, so its life probably cannot relegate certain functions for darkness and others for light. Being so close to its star, however, it orbits every thirty-seven days, so that a whole year takes roughly the same time as an Earth month. This passage of the seasons is accelerated tenfold compared to ours. This planet is close enough to our solar system that, standing on the planet, you can see our own sun. You may also be surrounded by life, quietly counting out a thirty-seven-day circannual rhythm.

Most exciting in this whole story of the body clock is what has not yet been told. New directions in research and new applications for existing revelations point the way for enormous changes in how we see biology and our place within nature. If interdisciplinary links emerge between circadian rhythms research and anthropological work—as this book seeks to cultivate—the understanding that follows may bring into question the way we blindly impose cultural practices on wildly varying environments without a thought to the practices that evolved, culturally, to respond to those conditions.

The field of medicine is where circadian rhythms can have the greatest impact in the near term. We now understand that, for each bodily process, there is a peak time of day. When testing for high blood pressure, it's not enough to take a reading—a doctor needs to also note the time of day to interpret that number in context. Some tests, like allergy trials, really should be done in the evening, outside of traditional clinic hours, for the most accurate results. Fever can no longer be determined by a set temperature threshold, since the body's evening temperature might be a full degree higher anyway as it cools the body for sleep. The same temperature in the morning is a more dire indication. Certain threadworm parasites are only to be found in blood tests during the day because they hide in the lungs at night.

Similarly, drug prescriptions should indicate the hour they should be taken—otherwise the dosage may be wildly approximate. Timed interventions that take advantage of the body clock are called *chronotherapy*. You'd best learn that word, because you're going to be seeing it a lot in the future. Whereas now drugs are typically administered during times that are convenient for the hospital or the patient, that is going to change.

Take chemotherapy. Cancer drugs typically target all rapidly dividing cells, which include cells in malignant tumours as well as cells in hair, in bone marrow and in the digestive system's lining. The side effects of cancer drugs include severe nausea, nerve problems and kidney damage. An oncologist wants to give the most aggressive dose possible to kill the cancer while keeping the side effects bearable. Like most things cancer-related, it's a heartbreaking business.

But like everything else in the body, tumour growth is rhythmic. Chronotherapy doses the body in sync with maximum tumour growth, while avoiding the times of day when, for example, the gut lining is replenishing itself. Certain lymphomas divide their cells between nine and ten o'clock at night. Compare that to the gut lining: At seven in the morning, its cells divide twenty-three times as much as in the evening. And bone marrow cell division peaks at noon. Knowing this, it seems reasonable to give chemotherapy in the evening, even though this is a very uncommon practice at present. If kidney damage is an issue, choosing a time when the kidneys increase urine flow can dilute the concentration of a dangerous drug, especially if the patient drinks a lot of water to mix it with. A recent colon cancer trial showed that patients with rhythmically oscillating meds could tolerate a 40 percent higher dosage and with less severe side effects. Doctors were able to reduce three times as many tumours by one-half or more in this group than in the regular chemo group. Similarly, a chronotherapy study on ovarian cancer halved the side effects and quadrupled the five-year survival rate.

In the early morning—at or before waking—blood pressure surges, dislodging plaque from arterial walls. If the plaque blocks a coronary artery, a heart attack can ensue, and, indeed, we see more heart attacks a little after this time. If blood pressure is above normal to begin with, there is a much higher risk of a heart attack—about five times as high. Most patients take their blood pressure medication with breakfast, and it takes a while to achieve full effect, so the drug's concentration in their blood is at its lowest during the early morning surge when it's needed most. Chronotherapy in this case is simply a matter of taking the pill at bedtime instead to last through the night and into the early morning. To defeat a disease, knowing its rhythms is much of the battle. The hormones secreted at night—growth hormone, estrogen and the like—are the same substances used in hormone therapies for delayed puberty, growth deficiencies and menopausal problems. Chronotherapy entails timing these infusions in sync with the existing circadian rhythm.

The daily peaks in the growth of tumours are even mimicked in yearly patterns. Different cancers have different seasonal peaks, but breast cancer is most likely to be first detected in spring—and least in fall—and chemotherapy side effects vary with the seasons too. Death from heart attack is much more likely in mid-winter than in summer and, for nine-to-five workers, it's most likely to happen on a Monday!

From chronotherapy and sleep aids to shift work and jet lag, there is nothing but room for growth in circadian rhythms research. Not only has the field not yet found its Einstein, it has yet to enjoy its Newton. There are just so many places the body clock can take us, and its link to anthropology—how people around the world structure their days and how they fit sleep into their lives—creates a potentially rich interdisciplinary field. My hope is that this book will encourage more exploration of this link, and that diversity in cultural daily rhythms will flourish and be protected from homogenization.

index